327 Ocean Street

A home away from home

Beau O'Kelly

To Niall, Paddy And Michael,

This is Just The Start of our World Wide Adventures!

Yarmouth!!
You're all Set man!

I'll See Ya at Girls Aloud!

slainte
publishing

First published in Ireland in 2005 by Slainte Publishing

Printed and bound in Ireland

Cover Design by Padraig McFadden
Cover Illustration by Barry Kennedy

ISBN 0-9549205-0-3

slaintepublishing@hotmail.com

Slainte Publishing
Firhouse
Dublin

Acknowledgement

I would like to extend my sincerest gratitude to all the fantastic friends I made in Cape Cod, and for the countless number of unforgettable times I experienced with you during the greatest summer of my life. Without everyone I have mentioned in this book, the three months I spent across the water wouldn't have been the same. You will be forever in my thoughts no matter where life takes me, and I hope you feel the same way, too.

> Go raibh míle maith agat chun
> na doaine speisialta atá i mo
> Shaoil. Tá mé i ngrá libh.

I must also thank my mad but world class mother, who gave me this seemingly crazy idea to begin with, when I asked her a day after I got home, 'so Mam, what now?' And to my family: my sister, who, with her wise words kept me on the right track, and my brother, who, with his dangerous suggestions nearly threw me off that track.

They always believed in me, and were confident that I could achieve the impossible.

A special thanks is owed to Raphael Ryan, one of the coolest teachers ever to grace a school corridor, and editor extraordinaire, who selflessly and tirelessly devoted his time to make sure this book gleamed with professionalism and respectability.

Fair play also, to two talented friends of mine who were responsible for the design and creation of such a wonderful cover: Barry and Podge – cheers lads.

Contents

1. Cheers America   9

2. Welcome to Hyannis   21

3. Banished from Ireland   24

4. Mr Miagi, you rat you   58

5. Ladderman and sidekicks go to town   84

6. Arnie?   108

7. Spirits visit at night when there is no light   121

8. Wow! – Our very own place   142

9. Not such an appetising White Russian   161

10. The Irish Rover lives on   183

11. DJ Bollocks   203

12. What a ride!   219

13. Inspector Plod   238

14. The Cape Cod sun gets ready to set   248

15. Out with a bang (and a bust)   259

16. Road Trip here we go!   265

It's been four days now since I've returned home from the Cape. The place still looms large in my mind. I'm saying things that are American; my body is here in Ireland, but my mind and soul are still in 327 Ocean Street. This past summer has had so much of an impact on my life, I feel compelled to record it in some way, shape or form. So this is my story.

Cheers America

1

'Mam! Do I have everything: passport, money, DS 2019 Form?'

(Don't forget this last form or you will be going back home for it. It happened).

'Stop worrying, you have everything.'

Thank God for mothers, great at easing the auld nerves.

At last the time had come. I was fairly tired from the night before, not from lack of sleep but my good friend next door called in with a farewell bottle of vodka, so obviously we had to drink that. The waiting and anticipation had finally come to an end. This would be the first time I would leave my family for real. Granted I went to Spain in third year with my class for three weeks and Majorca with friends after the Leaving Cert, but this was different. Those times were purely holiday situations, and even then I was unbelievably homesick. I wanted this so much I could taste it. The adrenaline was pumping through my veins like beer flowing from a tap on a Friday night. At the same time, I was nervous, nervous about living somewhere completely alien to Dublin for three months and nervous at getting so homesick after two or three weeks that I'd come running home with my tail between my legs. Despite these thoughts and fears, I couldn't wait to get out of the house and into my Mam's car to take that twenty-minute trip to Dublin Airport. Once my bags were thrown into the boot and my family and I were seated comfortably in the Corolla, I knew my adventure had started.

The Airport

Originally, I planned to go to the States alone, with the intention of working and experiencing being out in the big bad world by myself. Thankfully, that didn't go to plan. A few months back when I booked my flights, I met up with my good friend, Michael, one Friday night playing soccer in my old school. I told him my flights were booked and that I was headed for Cape Cod in Boston at the start of June. He made a passing comment that the group he would be going with (including his girlfriend), wanted to go to either San Diego or (you guessed it) the Cape. Low and behold, a week later, we would all be travelling together, same day, same flights. That's faith for ya. To be honest I was relieved. Going with a group of friends would be a lot more fun and a lot less daunting than going solo.

After barely managing to scrape together 1.30 for the toll bridge (we always forgot about that feckin' yoke), we arrived at departures. It was tough saying goodbye to the family I had grown so close to over the past year in particular. It had been a difficult year emotionally for me; my family acted as my rock, providing unshakeable love and support. Tears were shed and goodbyes were made. As tough as it was, I made my way over to the entrance, all the while looking back and waving to the people I was leaving behind.

As I made my way into the hustle and bustle of the lobby, it didn't take long to locate Michael. His girlfriend, Emma, and her friends were there, too. Emma hailed from Kerry and had met Michael in college. She had a delightfully friendly and charming nature along with a sense of humour that could take just about any joke or slag that was thrown her way. It broke a few girls' hearts when Michael fell in love with her. He was a slim good-looking fella, with an easygoing, magnetic personality who had plenty of admirers. But he didn't care; he had found his destiny in the attractive, outgoing Emma.

We all got to chatting. Every last one of us seemed to possess the same raw desire to get on the plane and experience American life for the summer. This, of course, wouldn't begin to happen for at least three hours. As a result of September 11, people flying outside Europe had to show up to allow security rustle through their cases with painstaking accuracy. It was a nuisance, but it did give us time for a few jars in the airport bar. The bar seemed to be free of any other summer adventure-seekers. It was only June 3rd, and relatively early to be leaving Ireland. Our early departure was in the hope of finding jobs and accommodation without too much hassle. So after five or six drinks, a feed from McDonalds and a considerable amount of anticipation, it was time to board EI106, which would hopefully bring us directly into Logan Airport.

The Airplane
Although we made up most of the travelling students on board, there was a real buzz in the air. Fortunately there were no delays. If there had been, I think we'd have all started bouncing off the little windows in the plane. The craic started almost as soon as we got on board (a few drinkies made sure of that). We filled the

plane with laughter, stories, jokes and most of all we talked of our plans for the summer. We felt free, we felt like eagles soaring through the skies; this summer would be great and we would make sure of that.

The stop-off in Shannon came upon us unnoticed, where we had to go through emigration. The plane would be ready to takeoff in forty-five minutes, just enough time to fill out all the forms and pick up some jar along the way. You'd be surprised how much can be drunk between Shannon and Dublin. After surviving the in-flight movie of Chicago and the magnificent five star meals we were served, we were ready for America. We were ready for a summer filled with adventure, for whatever experience, good and bad that would come our way. The question was: 'Was America ready for us?'

Boston Baby!

Let me off, let me off, let me off, Christ the excitement was too much to bear! I was waiting, not so patiently, to get off the bloody airplane. At last, movement.

'Come on hurry up, walk a little quicker would ya.'

I think we walked through the tunnel that linked the plane with the actual airport in record time; Linford Christie himself would have been left straggling. Now that we had disembarked, it shouldn't take too long for us to leave the airport. That's what I thought anyway. First we had to go through all the red tape and bureaucratic bullshit involved in travelling to the States. We were stopped several times along the way by burley security people inquiring as to the nature of our trip. Believe me, this is not the most pleasant of experiences. These people are as cold as steel, have faces that would scare Freddy Kruger, and possess snarls that would shame a Rotweiller. When we finally cleared the 'Labyrinth of Hell', without being arrested for something farcical such as having a teddy bear that looked like Saddam Hussein in our bags, we made our way to the arrivals hall.

Michael, Emma and I were staying in Boston that night while the rest of the girls, Maria, Laoibhse and Alyssa decided to head on towards the Cape. We had a slight problem though. I travelled with Usit, which meant that I had to stay over night in a designated hostel to attend a compulsory orientation in the morning, whereas Michael and Emma had already had an orientation back in Ireland some time ago. A bus would be there to pick up all the Usit travellers and I didn't want to be separated from them. When I saw the Usit Rep I asked him if it was possible for my friends to travel with us to the hostel. He was a young American and said if the bus wasn't full it would be no problem.

The bus would be a few minutes in coming. So we did as most Irish guys would do in our situation, we started playing soccer with Michael's miniature football that he brought with him. This helped pass the time, despite a few disapproving looks that were cast our way. There were a good few people waiting for the bus; most of them were foreigners from places such as Russia and Poland, while the remainder were Irish.

The bus had plenty of space to accommodate the extra two bodies. When we left the airport, one of the Reps gave us the tourist speech. We were also given handouts explaining the dangers of the city, places to eat, bus and taxi information, emergency phone numbers and so on. In no time at all we arrived at the Hostel International. Wow! What a place. This truly was a hostel to beat all other hostels. It resembled a hotel. It was huge. It looked like it should be housing rich tourists instead of semi-broke Irish students. This wasn't too shabby a place to be spending my first night in Boston, not too shabby at all.

Before we could be released into the wilds of this beautiful city, we had to check-in and be given (come on, you know this one) another chat. I think they believed we had never ventured outside our front doors before. At the front desk, we had to produce our passports and DS 2019 Forms. When you go to the US be prepared for all the paperwork and consequent delays and mild headaches you will inevitably experience. The hostel had a spare room for Michael and Emma. We asked if we could share a room, as each one contained four beds. This seemed like a reasonable request but the regulations-and-rules-following receptionist thought otherwise. Ah well, it was better than nothing, I figured.

Once we had thrown our bags into the rooms and freshened up a bit, (we didn't bother changing) it was time to explore Boston. Our first port of call was to get something to eat as we were gasping for a proper feed. There was a restaurant across the road called Pizzeria Uno, which sounded like the perfect place to grab some grub. The trickiest part in getting to this restaurant was trying to cross the road without being run over like the proverbial hedgehog. You had to make sure you looked the opposite way you do in Ireland, otherwise you'd be going home in a body bag.

Pizzeria Uno was a real American restaurant. It had TVs on most of the walls, each showing the baseball game (Fenway Park, home to the Boston Red Sox, was literally next door to us). Our waitress was a stereotypical American, all smiles and a personality that seemed as fake as Pamela Anderson's chest.

'Hi guys! How are you, can I get you a drink?'

I blame this apparent sucking up or overly nice syndrome on the tipping system they employ in the States. People working in the service industry such as pubs and restaurants, act as nice as Ned Flanders in order to get the best possible tip, and if this means kissing your ass, then so be it. We took up the nice waitress's offer of a drink and ordered three glasses of wine (why not, we were on this sprawling continent for the first time). As hungry as we all were, even our empty bellies couldn't handle the giant size portions we got. No wonder America has a problem with obesity, you could have fed the whole Irish football team on what we got. After a most relaxing first meal (except for the occasional interruption from the friendly waitress) we were ready to see the sights.

The sun was shining brightly in the Boston sky and the three of us, it seemed, were walking on air. The adrenaline that pumped around our bodies acted like a sort of drug, it was great. We were on such a high; we were seeing the sights and experiencing life in a foreign country with our new-found freedom. The city of Boston was more like a European city than an American one. Although it had its fair share of high-rise buildings, they weren't as awe-inspiring and certainly didn't possess the same type of raw magnificence as New York and other cities.

Surprisingly, the streets were quiet. You would have expected with the sort of weather they had to see hordes of people pushing past one another to try and squeeze into plush shops, or sun worshippers using the rays to brown their pale skin. But none of this was in evidence. The biggest assembly of people we saw was on Boston Commons; a beautiful park in the middle of the city that must have been home to thousands of squirrels and other wildlife. About twenty baseball players of differing genders were exploiting the calm, warm late afternoon to relax with a highly competitive ball game. Parked at the side of the road was a row of the biggest and most impressive stretch limos we had ever seen. The three of us came to the conclusion that the collection of men and women on the field must have been important to have a line of these elongated cars, with every window blackened out, waiting patiently until they were finished. We watched for a while hoping that they might invite us to join them.

On the way to the hostel earlier we saw Cheers, the famous pub from the classic TV programme. This, we decided as we drove by, would be the first pub we would grace in America. In order to get to Cheers, we had to get the T. This is what the underground was called and it cost a dollar each. It felt exhilarating to be travelling on the underground just like in the movies, although we were secretly hoping a junkie looking for cash to feed his habit wouldn't stab us.

We stood outside Cheers, which was called something different, (the name slips my mind at present) gazing at the overhead canopy that helped immortalise this great bar, and the famous stairwell that lay patiently below waiting to lead us downstairs and into Sam Malone's bar. There we could chat to the rest of the regulars and drink till the small hours. This wasn't to be, not because Sam and the boys weren't there, but because the bar itself wasn't the same bar used in the programme. Only the outside was used for filming. This was a gigantic disappointment; our dream of sitting at the counter where the lads had sat, maybe talking to Sam (in our imaginations anyway), would not come to pass. This bar was nothing special.

Around the back, souvenirs were sold. Being your typical tourist, I decided to buy a Cheers baseball cap, and a ball for Michael, even though it wasn't officially the same pub used for the programme. Since it was one of my favourite TV shows I had to buy some Cheers memorabilia. I would end up getting great use out of this cap as I wore it all summer long. I'm not a huge fan of baseball caps but you soon welcome wearing them with the different extremes of weather you experience. I got talking to the guy who was selling the merchandise and he said that there was a replica Cheers bar only a few minutes down the road. Ah, game on, I thought. He gave us directions and on we ventured.

'Jesus Ted, my feet are killin me,' I moaned as we entered our second hour trying to find this feckin' replica bar.

Every person we asked seemed to give us different directions. After what seemed like an age (our feet thought so anyway) we somehow managed to stumble across it. In the end this, too, was a let down. The bar counter itself was similar; the rest of the pub bore no resemblance to Cheers at all. At this stage we didn't care, we were parched and needed some alcoholic refreshment fast. It was quite late by the time we got there so we didn't stay long. A couple of pints later and we were out the door.

On the way back to the hostel, we stopped in Quincy Market. This was a huge food court offering delicacies from around the world. Although I was still pretty full from the meal and beer, I decided to buy some Chinese food just to say I had eaten there. It was part of an area called Faneuil Hall. This was the equivalent to Temple Bar in Ireland, only nicer. There were various pubs where people sat outside drinking and socialising. There were comedians and performing artists such as musicians and flamethrowers; the atmosphere in the place was fantastic. With the half eaten plastic tray of cheap Chinese safely tucked in my belly and the other half chucked away in the bin, it was time to hit the pillow and rest our weary legs for the long day ahead.

I was the first to awake from my slumber the next morning. I was sharing a room with an Italian and his friend who was from Northern Ireland. Once my eyelids had opened there was no closing them again. I jumped out of bed, washed, brushed my teeth and got dressed. The orientation was at 9am to be attended by all J1s (this is the name given to Irish college students who have obtained a temporary visa allowing them to live and work in America for the summer months). That gave me enough time to enjoy the continental breakfast that was part of the package. I called into Michael and Emma across the way. They were only getting out of bed and still had to beautify themselves. I told them I'd meet them downstairs for breaky; I was starving.

As I walked into the breakfast room, I noticed three or four boxes with food in them (just for me) at the end of the room. Donuts, four huge boxes of donuts, would you believe it. This was meant to be a continental breakfast. No toast or croissants, no sausages or rashers, only donuts. Continental breakfast my arse. I decided to eat a couple anyway; they were free and would fill me up for a while. As I was enjoying my luxury meal I got chatting to three lovely girls from Kerry. They were spending the summer on Nantucket – an island located an hour from Hyannis by boat.

After a quarter of an hour or so, Michael and Emma came strolling in, no doubt looking forward to their well deserved continental breakfast – since they did spend forty dollars each for the privilege of staying there. As unimpressed as I was, after we finished consuming our famine, we headed up to the orientation. This lasted about an hour. They gave us information to do with social security, jobs, accommodation, laws, living in the US, and so on. They also told us about Sevis.

This was a tracking system set up by the US Government after 9/11 to try and eliminate future terrorist attacks. Every J1 student was compelled to log onto the Sevis website and provide them with details about their job, where they were living, their social security number, that kind of thing. This allows the powers that be to track where and what immigrants are doing. If people fail to do this, they risk losing their sponsor for the remainder of their stay in the States and face the threat of not being allowed into the US again. With the ending of the orientation we were now free to do as we pleased and go where we wanted. We called for a taxi to take us to the bus station.

We travelled with the Kerry girls. They were going to stop in Hyannis because there was a social security office there; it would be quicker than trying to find one in Boston and having to wait in line for an aeon. The bus journey would take the guts of a couple of hours and the ticket cost $17. The bus was mostly full for the journey. We were all hyper and full of excitable energy. At the start everyone on the bus was quiet but, within a short time, all that would change.

People were attracted to our conversation through our loud laughing and constant joke telling. We talked to a pilot, a college guy, a potential future president of the United States (who funnily enough was one of the nicest guys we met that summer) and more. The bus was alive with hearty laughter and chitchat. On your average bus trip in America, silence would be all you could hear. I think the passengers on board were somewhat surprised yet pleased with the fun-filled atmosphere that enveloped the bus that afternoon. The potential president gave us his number and told us to call him if we had any problems, while the college guy told us to call him as he wanted to party with some mad Irish people. What a great start. We already had friends and contacts in this vast land.

Welcome to Hyannis

2

After a very enjoyable trip we had arrived in Hyannis, our new home for the next three months. We told the Kerry girls we would meet them at the social security office in about half an hour. First, we had to go and leave our bags somewhere. (Unfortunately by the time we got there the girls had gone; that was to be the last time we would see them during the summer). As we stepped off the bus we could be forgiven for thinking that somewhere along the way we had turned around and headed back to Ireland. We were greeted, not so kindly, by our old friend, Mr Heavy Rain, along with a chill in the noon air. We stood at the station wondering where to go. The rest of the girls were staying at a local motel but we had no idea of its location.

As we struggled to come up with a solution, out of nowhere a black Mercedes pulled up beside us. The tinted window on the passenger side rolled down to reveal a slightly older than middle-aged woman sitting in the car. She asked us if we needed a lift. As strange as this proposal was, it was pissing rain and we were only too happy to accept a ride off this stranger. She asked us if we had jobs or a place to live for the summer. We said we didn't. She offered us jobs straight away working in her car park. Our duty would be to stand at the entrance and try to encourage motorists to come in and use her facility to park their cars, while they hopped on the boat and went across to one of the islands. She would pay us $8 an hour and expect all of us to work between 50 and 60 hours a week. I had always believed we would be able to find jobs quickly but I never believed it would take us less than a minute. But we hoped for something better. So we took her number and said we'd be in touch, even though we had no intention of accepting her offer. So the strange lady dropped us off at the motel, which in actual fact was just beside the bus station.

The motel looked as authentically American as you can get. At the front was the reception area, while the rooms were situated around the back. They were laid out in two long rows, parallel to each other, with an upstairs and downstairs row. In the middle was the car park. We couldn't check in straight away; the rooms were being cleaned, so we left our bags beside the indoor swimming pool and headed out for a spot of lunch. The effects of the donuts had long since worn off, leaving a gaping gap in our bellies. We went to the first restaurant we saw which, again, was just across the road from the station. It was still raining as we stepped into the Sunny Side Diner (must have imported the name). It was plain but dry. We spotted the other girls sitting down the far end having their lunch so we joined them. Our chicken burgers (sandwiches, as the Yanks call them) and chips (fries) were well and truly wolfed down.

The motel we were staying in was called the Best Value Inn. It had been bought a couple of months earlier by a Chinese family. The American who owned it originally now owned another motel in the middle of Main Street, along with a restaurant-come-pub. The new owners were in the process of revamping the place.

In all honesty, they needed to. The outdoor pool, which we were looking forward to using, looked like a swamp. I wouldn't have been surprised if it housed a family of alligators in the murky waters that fed on the eels they were co-habiting with. Easily said, we never took the opportunity to find out.

The rooms themselves were very basic. Their main flaw was the absence of a fridge. This was a little annoying because it meant we would have to drink warm beer and everyone knows warm beer is putrid. I think we would have preferred to have a fridge rather than a TV. After checking in, it was time to go and explore our new surroundings.

The only thing we did that evening was to go for a bite to eat, as the rain was persistent in its downpours. To our pleasant surprise there was a Hooters restaurant in the town. For everyone who doesn't know what this is, and as the name suggests, it is a restaurant that employs big breasted, beautiful looking girls to serve their customers while providing some attractive visual stimulation. The girls wear tight hot pants along with an even tighter top that seems to accentuate their breasts very nicely. Most of them, however, are IQ deficient Barbie dolls that wouldn't know the real purpose of a dictionary, other than resting a portable mirror on. Due to the nature of the service, and the scenery that accompanies it, it's every man's dream restaurant. After dinner we stopped in at the local liquor store to pick up a few cans for the night, and to warn the employees that they would be seeing a great deal of us in the coming months.

As we'd be haunting the place like ghosts.

3 **Banished from Ireland**

Cape Cod is a long island that juts out into the ocean. It takes the form of a flexed arm. Hyannis isn't the biggest place in the world; in fact most of the action took place on one main street. Away from this street there isn't much for tourists to do. All the shops and restaurants were pretty much located here. Most of the shops were small independently run stores; you didn't get the bigger, more popular outlets in town. A lot of the shops existed solely to cater for tourists, with copious amounts of T-shirt and souvenir shops. Then you had an internet café, a few banks, quaint restaurants that had seating arrangements outside as well as in, two or three ice cream parlours (including Ben And Jerry's), and some pubs. That was about it. It certainly wouldn't appeal to the hard-core shoppers but there was always the mall on the edge of town for that type of thing. You'd wonder how the shops survived during the long winters but I'd imagine most of them would close.

One of the first things that hits you as you stand on the side of Main Street is the size of the cars – they were colossal. Our cars back home look like children's toy pedal cars by comparison. A lot of people drove jeeps or, as they call them, SUVs. With the roads being so wide for the most part, they can easily accommodate these monster-like vehicles. Even the normal cars were huge, with most of them possessing four, five and six litre engines. V6 and V8s were the style, and automatics the norm. Hyannis is quite a wealthy town. It attracts people such as the Kennedys, Arnold Schwarzenegger and other big names, and where these names are you can be guaranteed an extravagant showing of automobiles.

The Terminator himself drove a chrome-encrusted Hum V. Works of art such as Dodge Vipers, Ferraris, Hum Vs, Porsches and others flaunted their curvy metal bodies for all to see; for the car lover this place is 'pure Disney'. There was also a large selection of vintage cars that would, no doubt, fetch a tidy sum at auction. A popular pastime in Hyannis was to cruise down Main Street every so often in your beautiful car letting everyone see how rich and important you were.

As we strolled down Main Street, it felt like we were alone. The place was empty, like a town that just had a nuclear bomb dropped on it. Puddles of water lay scattered along the roads and paths. The sky was dull; it resembled a winter's day back home, and even had the cold air to boot. Tumbleweed blowing down the rain-soaked road, like in the movies, wouldn't have looked out of place. Hyannis looked depressed and ugly. A lot of the shops were closed. Were they shut for good because there was nobody around to keep them in business? In my mind, Hyannis portrayed one of those scary abandoned towns you'd regularly read about in a Stephen King novel; I was expecting a psychotic Jack Nicholson to walk by any minute. What was wrong with this place? I wondered if we had made a huge mistake coming to the Cape.

Cleverly enough I had chosen not to bring a jacket with me, and not just that, I had also neglected to pack a jumper. Why would you need these items of clothing during the summer in America, I pondered, as I filled my backpack a couple of days ago in my room.

We had a house to view that day. Before I go on, let me tell you that most of the landlords, and especially the landladies over there, don't like boys. They think we're wild animals that would no doubt bring home tons of girls, have out-of-control, up-all-night parties, and would inevitably destroy the house. They certainly had us figured out. They must have been studying up on the male species of the Irish race weeks before we arrived.

The house we were to view was on Sea Street, a long monotonous road that poked out from the bottom of Main Street. On our way there, we encountered a few young guys. A couple of them were hassling the girls. I wondered if they had seen any girls over the long bleak winter. The ladies however didn't fall for their cunning pulling tactics that consisted of a few hopeless chat-up lines and my personal favourite, the trousers around the knees while showing off the boxers trick. One of the guys asked me for a cigarette. I hadn't got one because I didn't smoke (apart from the twice-weekly cigar, that is). I told him I had none, so in retaliation he made one of those seemingly cool hand gestures that are so expertly done by the hommie community and spat.

'You tourists suck, man!'

Charming. I hoped all the rest of the residents in the town didn't feel the same as this spanner. It occurred to me though that every summer hundreds of Irish amadáns flock to this place to live and party. It could well be possible that the locals had become sick of the Irish and their crazy antics over the years.

We arrived at the house. It was made of wood, like most of the houses in Hyannis. We walked up the pathway through the small over-grown garden and knocked on the door. A weird looking woman opened the old decaying wooden door and invited us in. Cautiously we entered her house. There was a giant of a man sitting in the living room, possibly her husband or perhaps some fiend she had asked over to scare the shite out of the wild Irish, dissuading them from running her out and capturing her house. He succeeded. We looked around downstairs first, hastily, as we feared the ape on the couch may be hungry and he'd see us as appetizing lunch.

Upstairs there were three bedrooms and enough beds for us all. Despite this advantage it was a dark house. There was no life to it. I think that was the way the scary woman liked it. It turned out that the landlady and her man actually lived next door in the other part of the house. They had rules about visitors not being allowed over after eleven at night and did not allow parties to take place in any way, shape or form: bollocks to that. There had been some debate between Michael and I with the other girls about the house, but when we heard of their living arrangements we quickly came to an agreement about not staying there. We were in America for a summer of fun, not to live by the Ten Commandments.

As we walked back towards the motel I had thoughts of leaving this depressed area and going elsewhere in the US. There was more life in a graveyard on the outskirts of a small village in the North Pole. There was no sign of any Irish people. Actually there was no sign of any people for that matter, except for a few nutty individuals and some cool hommies. We decided against it, giving the place a chance to pick up and grant us that brilliant summer we were searching for.

A couple of days had passed and the weather was still unchanged. Fleeting images of my wet gear hanging in my wardrobe at home plagued my ability to think clearly. We took the opportunity to do a bit of wet sightseeing. The beach was the first thing on our agenda. This, too, looked bleak and grey. It wasn't looking good, I didn't know how much more of this place I could take. When you hear the name Cape Cod, a picture of beauty comes to mind with a cloudless blue sky and stunning young girls strolling down the road wearing nothing more than bikinis. I hoped these things would start to appear, although looking around for the life of me I couldn't see how.

The small amount of Americans we had talked to, said the season would take a couple of weeks to take off. Once that happened, they assured us plenty of tourists would be swarming the place. This sounded promising. Little by little, positive signs of life were starting to emerge. One day as we were walking down Main Street, maybe after seeing the world's ugliest beach, a black pick-up truck stopped beside us. There was a guy and a girl in the truck. The guy leaned over and told us about a local nightclub that was starting on Thursday night, called the Blue Room. The girl, who was quite pretty, gave us flyers for the club. Yes, there was life in the place, even if it did sound like a gay club. We would definitely be there to check it out.

Every now and then Michael and myself met Irish people who were just arriving. Before I came away, my plan was to make as many friends as I possibly could here. At home, I have the same friends that I've had for the past few years, my best friends being from my secondary school whom I didn't get to see enough of, two or three friends from college as well a couple of good friends in my area whom I've been friends with for as long as I could remember. One of these was away in Germany for the year so I didn't see him much. It was a lonely enough year, and I was determined next year wouldn't follow the same pattern as the one just gone. As great as my friends were, I needed some new people in my life. I needed a change that would see some new influences come into the fray. Anyway, what would be the point in coming to America without this goal in mind to a certain extent.

From the outset, Michael, who was my best friend from school (probably because of our semi-similar personalities and mutual feelings for doing things we shouldn't be doing) and myself were determined to get to know as many people as we could. I hoped this would lead to many strong friendships and would also help to connect all the Irish that were over here for the summer. (This, in turn – would lead to many a legendary party).

A large number of these first time travellers were checking into the Best Value Inn. One of the first groups to check-in consisted of about six or seven guys and girls from Dublin. When we realised they were staying in the motel, myself and Michael called up to them for a few sips. We chatted away for a while – they were a sound bunch of lads.

The next to arrive were two guys from Cork and two girls from Mayo. They had come over on the same plane and through this got to know each other. The four of them decided to share a room together as it would work out a lot cheaper (you paid a set room rate regardless of how many people occupied it). One of the girls lost her vanity case on the way over. It had been sent to Egypt in some heinous mistake. When she got it back a few days later, it was totally destroyed. All she was left with was a toothbrush, shampoo and conditioner. Why the fuck someone would come all the way out to Hyannis just to return these items, along with a battered vanity case is beyond me.

Soon enough the motel was half full with Irish students. The other half was made up of trailer trash. There was a woman there who had a voice like a dying hyena. Every time she talked, you felt like either filling your ears with cotton wool to drown out the insane shrieking noise or giving her such a punch to the head that you knocked her out cold. She had a husband and a child. I felt sorry for them both; it was going to be a long life.

There were also a hefty percentage of black people staying in the motel. It was funny because for a long time, the Irish and the blacks were treated like slaves by the Americans. Both races were a minority, and as a result worked all the harder, more labour-intensive jobs. It is common knowledge, too, that we damn near built America together. I wondered, looking around me, had things changed that much. Here the two races were living in a kip of a place just like old times.

There was a black couple staying next door to us. They actually lived there. Their whole world revolved around this one lowly motel room and their minivan, which Larry, the husband, had bought for $100 and was permanently parked outside their room. Michael and myself became good buddies with them. Larry worked in a furniture shop and also dealt in bikes, in both selling and repairing them. This was his main source of transport. He hadn't enough money to buy and insure a car, but his bike was a beauty; it was an old-fashioned one that you stopped by slamming the pedals into reverse.

A group of guys from Cork moved in across the way from us. As we are all aware, in Ireland there can sometimes be inter-county tension between different people. In this, I don't believe. Actually, let me put it a different way. Let me see, how can I sum this up, oh yes: what a load of crap. I am of the opinion that we are all equal, no matter what county we come from; none of us are superior or inferior to the other. I know that the accents, traditions, and ways of doing things differ from place to place but variety is the spice of life and should be respected, not judged. I'm from Dublin, born and bred, but I don't consider myself exclusively as a Dub. Don't get me wrong, I have nothing against where I live or where I'm from, but first and foremost I consider myself Irish. I wanted to meet folk from all over and make friends with people of every persuasion. I have been living in the county for twenty-one years and know my fair share. Now I desired to meet people from different places with different backgrounds, people who could teach me new things and open up new experiences for me.

To my pleasure this was happening thick and fast. Our group was rapidly integrating with the gang from Cork across the way. Nevaeh was the girl whose vanity bag had found its way to Egypt. She had flaming red hair (which she denied) and possessed a razor-sharp dry wit along with a fantastic hearty laugh, which, when you heard it, made you want to crack up even if the joke wasn't funny. She seemed a bit mad in the head and always up for a laugh, which is the type of person you need for a summer in a foreign country. You'd be guaranteed some weird and wonderful times. Clare, Nevaeh's best friend from home, was the quieter of the two, though nevertheless open and friendly. Not many people could be as vociferous as Nevaeh.

There were many more Irish people resident in the motel, not just the ones I've described. Within no time, Michael and I were on friendly terms with the majority of them. The effort spent getting to know people early on – if you could even call it effort – was more like a pleasure, was well worth it. There was an excitable air around the motel. Nobody we had met had made long-term accommodation arrangements.

After a few days, as people began settling in, talk of staying in the motel for the summer was beginning to spread. I thought this was a fine idea. All your friends would be around you. The feeling of pure freedom we felt was extremely liberating. The notion of being able to just go and talk or hang out with whoever you wanted without having to ring them first or drive miles across the city to see them was a real bonus. If you didn't want to do anything, you could just lie on the bed watching the weather channel praying the weather picked up sometime before September. No one had prior arrangements or plans; we were all in the same boat. It was like we were back in our childhood with no worries, no grown-up social rules, no barriers, just a utopian type of carefree existence. In saying that, it was also the start of our adulthood. We had to survive in America the length of a season, and we had to go out there and make the friends we craved and the life we sought.

*

During the first few days, Michael and myself were out doing a bit of sightseeing. In America, you can nearly always tell the Irish apart from the Americans. There is just something there that is completely different and totally unique. Maybe it was the pale white skin and red noses. We saw a couple of white girls across the road who, we thought had to be Irish.

It was a great feeling to be able to just walk over and talk to them. If you tried doing this at home, people would think you belonged in a home for nutters. They appreciated the effort and enjoyed meeting new people and getting to know new faces just as much as we did. It was nearly like starting life all over again. You had to go back to basics and do things such as make friends and form acquaintances. They, in turn, would help you to successfully get by for the duration of your stay while also feeding your soul and emotions with the type of stability and confidence we all need. If people were lost or needed help with a problem it was nice to have someone you could rely on. When you arrive you don't know anybody, so it's good to try and remedy this situation as soon as you can. Usually, the people you get to know from the start often turn out being your closest friends at the end.

There was a multitude of Cork folk on the Cape. I wondered if there were any people left at home still wandering Patrick Street (Cape Cod was later renamed Cape Cork when the American population dropped down to second place in the nationality standings). The two girls from Cork were bang on and were staying in the Cascade Motel, directly across from the Best Value Inn. They were expecting a friend from home, who had spent the last year or so living in Australia and other such exotic places, to arrive in a couple of weeks. We exchanged invitations to each other's motel rooms for drinks and continued on our sightseeing adventure.

That first week Michael and I bought a couple of bikes. We were sick to the teeth of walking everywhere; it was too feckin' tiring. Bike Zone was the local shop that sold second-hand bikes and at that point in time we had no idea that Larry was in the market. The selection to choose from was abysmal. As we were the first of the Irish community to buy bikes we managed to pick up some semi-decent ones. I bought a racer for $60 and Michael bought a mountain bike for $75. Despite being about forty-years old, and apparently one of the ugliest fuckin' bikes on the Cape, my racer was blessed with Cheetah-like speed. No other bike could touch her in a race. Thinking back now, I should have raced people for money; I would have made a small fortune.

Michael's bike was not born with the gift of pace. It did however have probably the most comfortable saddle ever created by man. It was like sitting in an armchair; all it was missing was somewhere to put your beer but I had every faith in Michael that he could construct some sort of jar holder. Once we bought locks, all that was left to do was give names to our faithful steeds. My racer would be named Martha, after Martha Stewart, one of the most recognisable household women in the US (I promise, the name just came to me). Michael's would be known as Honey Bunny.

The bikes were a Godsend. We could now travel around the place quickly and without too much stress on our legs. Hyannis for the most part was flat in layout. We were officially the first Irish people to own crappy second-hand excuses for bikes. We even had our very own parking space for the girls right outside our room in the motel. This was sweet. We were so proud of our trusty new semi, free-flowing fillies. We were warned by the salesman in Bike Zone about the risks of riding a bike in Hyannis. He said the drivers were lunatics and we should be very careful on the roads (I wonder if that meant we shouldn't drink a keg full of beer and cycle). We took his comments on board, loosely in any case, like most naive Irish students would.

At the start, we pretty much kept to the paths or side walks. Crossing the roads was a hazardous business since the cars came at you from the wrong direction. Some of the roads were also organised into one-way systems, which added to our confusion. We had a couple of sticky moments until we got a bit more familiar with the traffic situations. You literally had to have eyes at the back of your head. It's not that the Americans were bad drivers or that they hammered down the roads because, by and large, they kept to the speed limit which was quite slow in a lot of places. They drove aggressively, yet far too courteously. There were many times they would let you switch sides or make a turn when they really shouldn't because they held up traffic behind them. We were prepared to wait and, in fairness, expected to wait till we could cross the road or join another road.

The most important factor when you were cycling was to know the roads – which way they went, the one-way systems stuff like that. It was also important to drive close to the curb. Most of the drivers had no fear in passing you even if there was an oncoming car heading your way and it was a narrow road. I noticed their fondness for breaking the traffic lights, too. This was another factor to look out for as you flew down the road at breakneck speeds with bandy breaks.

Hyannis was now at our mercy. Michael and myself had the freedom of transport to explore the town and surrounding areas in more detail. The mall was the first thing on our list. When you watch programmes and films on TV at home, the young people always hang out at the malls; it seemed like the in place to be. It would be interesting to see if they were better than our shopping centres at home (would the Cape Cod mall measure up to The Square in Tallaght I wondered). The mall was about a ten-minute cycle from the motel. Locking our babies to the railings, we strolled in.

The mall was a long building and was all the one level. We decided to walk from start to finish, allowing us to see everything the place had to offer. In a lot of respects it was very similar to our malls. It had a good vibe and atmosphere to it. It was a place where you could stay for as long as you liked because it felt homely. All the famous shops were there – Fileens, Macys and the other giants that dominated the retail scene. These were the bigger stores that sold a whole range of merchandise from clothes to jewellery at competitive prices.

Along the way, there were luxurious leather armchairs that gave you massages right in the middle of the mall. Excellent, you definitely didn't find these in The Square. We had to give these babies a try, a dollar for three minutes, who could argue with that. A blend of pain and pleasure, I think enduring these chairs once would be enough. One shop we didn't particularly warm to was the pet shop (I think most Irish people would feel the same way). This wildlife shop sold every sort of pet from rabbits to racoons. The sad bit though was the dogs. They had a whole selection of canines that were imprisoned in small steel cages. They barked and howled to be released from captivity. Normally three were kept in the window of the shop for all the passers-by to come over and ogle.

'Ah, look at him, isn't he cute!'

You could almost see the life force being sucked out of these lovely animals. In saying that, they were being treated to a sort of circus spectacle. They got to stare and laugh at people that were either fat enough to fill a Beatle car, or so ugly that there was a reward offered for whoever could successfully cover their mug with a brown paper bag. I thought of buying two and freeing the rest. I didn't because I feared the security guard would raise his gun, take aim, and shoot me as I made a runner for the door with the dogs. We didn't make a habit of gracing that shop too often as it made us angry seeing what type of life they had to endure.

Carrying on, we came across another type of massage. It was called a hydro massage. It involved lying down in a machine-type waterbed. From the outside it looked as if people were actually being massaged by water. This wasn't exactly the case. You took off your shoes and lay on a normal bed, similar to a hospital bed, that had a hole cut at one end where you could comfortably put you head. The top is pulled over you, equivalent to a tanning bed. Water is then sprayed from jets at high speeds over your body, which was protected by a soft waterproof cover that prevented you from getting wet. You were given a handheld controller, which allowed you dictate the level of water intensity and choose which part of your body you wanted to massage (I recommend the feet and ass – very soothing).

Feeling relaxed and rejuvenated, we headed towards the Hooters stall which was in view from the hydro massage. No trip to the mall would be complete without a chat with an adequately ample Hooters girl.

After this we headed towards the food court, which was at the far end of the mall.

There was about six or seven different restaurants including McDonalds (obviously), a Chinese, a Japanese, a sandwich bar and so on. A plate of fried rice with two different meats was $5.45. Employees of the Chinese and Japanese restaurants stood outside giving free titbits of their offerings in the hope of tempting people to buy their food. Throughout the summer this would become a ritual of mine, walking around picking up free snacks off the very liberal Orientals. By the end, I think they had my picture up on the wall with a caption underneath, saying: 'Don't Give This Man Anymore Free Samples'.

There was also a games arcade and a big bookshop called Barnes And Noble beside the food court. The bookstore, to some, acted as a welcome escape from the everyday turmoil. It provided sumptuous armchairs where you could lose yourself in some fantasyland unknown to the rest of civilisation. If you were ever bored or just liked to read, this made a great pastime and helped fend off any stress you might be feeling.

With each passing day, more and more bikes were appearing outside rooms in the motel. They were starting to recognise the benefits cycling brought. One day this head-case in a white van stopped beside us in the motel car park. He said he had a load of cheap bikes to sell. He was flogging them for about twenty-five or thirty dollars. Great! We had just forked out double that for ours. It didn't matter, Honey had her bottom-hugging saddle and Martha was faster than a Chinese man forcing a piece of batter-wound chicken down your gullet. Toys R Us also invaded the market selling new bikes for $80. Although some acquired their bikes from the guy in the van, most went to Toys R Us. They sold pristine mountain bikes that had springy suspensions acting like shock absorbers – it was like riding a pogo stick, or a McDonalds employee, maybe. The different styles and outlandish colours were hilarious to behold. This was a fantastic way to get around. It was lovely to be able to go out into the fresh air, with the sun on your back, and head off wherever you liked; it also provided some welcome exercise. And when you were out there, cruising the streets, you felt as free as a bird in full flight. It seemed to have a surprisingly calming effect on us bikers.

During the first few days a lot of the shops were shut and the restaurants were closing at ten. The place would take a while to awake from its winter slumber.

We were starting to get cosy living in the Best Value Inn. There was a constant stream of new arrivals making their presence felt with every passing day, and the place began to come alive. We had begun making regular visits to people's rooms to enjoy a few cans of Cape Cod's finest cheapest beer. It didn't take long for people to hit it off – the consequence of moving to a foreign country. The benefit of staying in this motel was its central location. It was situated on Main Street, beside the bus station, or 'transportation centre' as the locals called it. This made it more accessible to welcome the recently arrived travelling Irish. The other positive factor was the amount of Irish who stayed there – it was like an Irish (drunken) summer camp. The craic was mighty and the atmosphere was second to none. By now, Michael was starting to come around to the idea of living there for the summer.

Four of us were staying in my room. There was Michael and I, who shared a bed. Then there was

Emma, Michael's girlfriend, who shared the other double bed with Alyssa, one of Emma's best friends from home. Alyssa's boyfriend, Jack, was coming over to join us in about two weeks. He had to wait at home for a meeting with the head of his college. It was a comfortable arrangement for the four of us, though you wouldn't want to wake up too many mornings with that special feeling and the surprise that accompanied this feeling. I was very fond of Michael but not in that sort of way, you understand. The pair of us did have to get used to the constant bellowing and hissing of hair dryers and hair straightners, though by the end of the summer, we were experts in the field of girls' fashion accessories and beauty. I can assure you my future wife will be very impressed with my vast array of knowledge on all things female.

The rest of the girls in our group had taken a room across the way. Two of them, Laoibhse and Maria, were here from the start, and two more, Sheila and Shauna, were coming in a week or so. The first pair were in the same class in college, so they were quite close. The absent duo, I had never met, but the more the better was my attitude.

Before the week was over I started looking for a job. I figured since we were among the first students to arrive we wouldn't have any problems finding work. We had applied for social security numbers earlier that week. Most establishments and places of employment demanded you have a social security number. It basically proves that you are legally entitled to work in the States. To be eligible for social security, you must first produce a valid work visa. This helps to crack down on the number of illegal aliens working and living in the US.

Every year, thousands of Mexicans manage to crawl through the barbed wire and sneak passed the dogs to try and carve out a better existence for themselves and their families. The standard of living in America is far higher to that of their native land. Unfortunately for them, in most cases, they can't qualify for social security, which in turn means that places that do employ them tend to treat them like slaves, and since they have no rights, they can't do anything about it. It would take a couple of weeks to receive our social security cards.

Michael and I went around to the different restaurants and bars filling out applications. We were getting a lot of positive feedback. Some places said they were looking for people and others told us to call back in a couple of days. Ah, this would be a piece of cake. We'd both have jobs in no time. The pair of us fancied waiter work because the tips were meant to be brilliant. We also tried the ferry company to see if they needed staff either on the boats or as dockhands. After spending a couple of long days pounding the pavement on the work trail, all we needed to do now was sit back, wait a few days, and we would be the newest employees in America.

*

As we patiently waited to join the working elite, we were determined to make the most of our spare time, and in particular, our spare nights. That first Thursday, we headed out to the Blue Room, the club we hoped wasn't gay. It was tucked in behind a restaurant just off Main Street. There was an entrance fee of five dollars if you were over twenty-one. You were then given a band to put around your wrist meaning you were permitted to drink alcohol. As we discovered, America's rules concerning underage drinking were as strict as their policies concerning terrorists.

The Blue Room looked like a big house party. There were a few different rooms and four different bars. A medium-sized dance floor dominated the middle of the 'house', which didn't see much action that first night. There was a room around the back, which was sort of like a 'chill-out' room. High tables and chairs, with unbelievably comfy leather seats decorated the room. I could tell I'd be spending a lot of time planted on those babies.

That night, there were very few people looking to party, either American or Irish. On the Cape, nightclubs close at a disrespectfully early time of 1am. We couldn't believe it when the lights came on at 12.45 and the bouncers were ushering us out the door bang on the stroke of 1; what a load of number 2! Things would only be getting started around that time at home. This did not impress us at all at all, in fact we pretty much bad mouthed this poxy law all the way home. Didn't the US Government know the Irish were coming for the summer? You'd imagine they might have tweaked the constitution a wee bit to make us feel more at home.

Well, I knew one thing anyway: 1 o'clock in the morning was too early to be hitting the sack, so we would have to initiate some sort of tradition, such as beach or house parties to keep the nights alive after the club doors had shut.

The night after the Blue Room fiasco Michael and myself decided to go to the Irish pub at the end of Main Street for a few pints. He was having dinner with his beloved so I told him I'd meet him there at about ten. I put on some semi-decent clothes and headed out to The Nine Famous Irishmen (who these were meant to be I hadn't a clue). Why in the world I got dressed up I'll never know because by the time I got there, I was wetter than an English hen party in Galway on a dirty weekend.

I decided to sit at the bar. There was nothing really Irish about the place. I'd seen more authentic Irish bars in the wilds of Kenya. The barman, or tender as he's called came over to me. He was a short guy with glasses and looked like the swot that was present in just about every secondary school classroom across the country. He asked me what I'd like to drink and I said a pint. All of a sudden there seemed to be a shift in his demeanour. With the finest of Cork accents he asked where in Ireland I was from. I hadn't noticed an accent when he spoke at first. I was probably daydreaming, trying to figure out who the nine famous Irishmen were, and so far I had only come up with Paul McGrath, Bosco and Dougal. So we got talking. He told me he had been over here for the past six years and had worked here ever since. He was from Ballinspittle in Cork and I told him I was from Dublin.

About twenty minutes after I arrived at the pub Michael strolled in, just as wet as I was. It was a good laugh, even if there weren't many people in the bar. A young American couple were perched on two stools beside us. They were around our age. They began talking to us and seemed pleasant enough. She was a bit madder than he, and every now and then he would say her name in complete disgust when she made, what seemed to him, an inappropriate comment. We each bought rounds of shots. Come the end of the night the couple were ready for the bed. Well she was anyway, horny bitch.

The bar was closing in fifteen minutes so we bought another couple of pints for the road (the cycle home). At one stage nature was calling so I told Michael I'd be back in a minute (eh, better make that a couple of minutes). On my way back to the bar I overheard the barman tell Michael he was from Blarney. That was strange, he had told me he was from Ballinspittle. Sitting down on the stool I said to the so-called Corkman that he told me he was from a different place altogether. His jaw dropped, and he vehemently denied he ever said he was from there. He walked away from us and I told Michael I was positive he said he was from Ballinspittle.

About two minutes later he came over and announced they were closing and we'd have to leave. We still had a little bit of drink left in the glasses and said we'd be finished in a minute. With a look that would send shivers shooting down your spine, he told us, in a loud tone of voice, that we had to go, now. I think the little man was trying to scare us. Staring him in the eye I said to him.

'You're not from Cork at all, are you?'

With that he started banging out orders for us to leave, and he even came around to our side of the bar. I didn't like the way he was treating us, and I took offence at him pretending to being an Irishman, probably in the hope of scoring better tips. I told him in no uncertain terms that he was a prick and a fake who wasn't welcome in our country. Two big bouncers came over and asked what the problem was. I told them that the barman was a wanker and didn't have the right to call himself Irish. As you can imagine, the bouncers politely asked us to leave in a way that suggested that if we didn't go at once, the relevant authorities would find our bodies dangling from a pole somewhere in the morning. As we left, we managed to hurl a few more home truths in the direction of swotacus, who conveniently stood behind the men of iron who were busy seeing us out.

The only Irish pub in the town, if you could call it that, and we were barred from it before the week was out. To be honest, I wouldn't have gone back there anyway except, maybe, to have thrown a hardback A4 size map of Ireland at the barman's head. At least it made for an interesting night and would be a good story to tell at the next get-together we had.

The courtyard in the motel was quite large, and for the most part there were very few cars parked there, especially during the daytime. Taking advantage of this, Michael's mini-football came in handy when it wasn't raining. Playing a bit of soccer helped keep inactivity at bay. This didn't last long. The owner of the motel, Mr Miagi, as we affectionately dubbed him, didn't appreciate our little kickaround. He came over the first time he saw what we were doing and told us we'd have to stop. In his best English, which was pathetic at best, he said if people saw us playing football from the road they would be put off coming to stay in the motel. Ah yes, this made perfect sense.

Holiday-makers who saw people enjoying themselves would most definitely freak out and take their business elsewhere – where the mood was a bit more depressed. That might be the way in China, I thought, but not in the happier western world.

Yet, not many customers seemed keen to give the motel even a casual glance, never mind stay there. We caused in all $0 damage, it wasn't possible with the ball we were using. I strongly believed that it was the sewage stricken, disease-infested swimming pool that might have influenced people's decisions whether to stay or not, and not our simple passing game. We ceased playing football and turned our attention to catch instead. As you would expect, we didn't get away with playing this activity for long either. Mr Miagi scurried over like a rabbit on a promise.

'No! You cannot throw ball to each other.'

Well, that was the end of our ball-playing days because I couldn't think of anything else we could do with it, apart from maybe ramming it where the sun don't shine up Mr Miagi.

We found out from some promoters that there was another nightclub in the town. It ran an Irish night every Sunday and the first one was a day away. We figured it had to be better than the Blue Room, where we were virtually the only people there on Thursday.

We were also invited to a house party by a couple of girls from Cork that same night. We had planned to go to this, as a sort of entrée before heading to the club. But when we went to the liquor store to buy some drink we were in for a nasty surprise. Take note ladies and gentlemen: in America, the liquor stores close on a Sunday. Ah! What a fuckin' hideous rule I hear you say. Well I totally agree, and we made this mistake a couple of times before we finally got it into our thick heads. This meant we had to go dry on a Sunday unless we had some drink left over from the festivities on the Saturday night. I think the government must have known that Irish night was on a Sunday, so they brought in the law to prevent us from getting too drunk and troublesome. Okay, we'd miss the party, but we could still buy drink in the bar when we got there. All was not lost.

Half the lads had 'fluid reserves', but the other half were as dry as a camel's arse in a sandstorm. The wealth was shared so no one went without. How could you leave an Irish person to fend for him or herself with no alcohol, that would be a crime against humanity (or at least St Patrick). Once we had downed a few pre-club beers and shoved on the glad rags, we were ready to search for the ultimate night out and find the holy grail of nightclubs. We left at around half nine because, as we found out on Thursday, the feckin' clubs close when it was time for the kids to be tucked in, or at least that's what it felt like. The rest of the gang stayed in the room drinking for a while, mainly because many of them were under twenty-one. They had to get nicely sauced up before going out, as they were sure to become temporary pioneers in the club.

We hadn't a clue where the club was, though it went by the name 'Pufferbellies'. It had to be the strangest name for a nightclub I'd ever heard. We had just walked out of the motel when a car pulled up beside us. In it were four American beauties wanting to know the way to Pufferbellies. What a coincidence. They were surprised to hear we were from Ireland and seemed interested. A couple of minutes later we passed the local food mart, which later became known as Apu's for obvious reasons. The girls stopped and went in to ask where the club was. We went over and they gave us directions. Gift. We said we'd see them there and off they went.

About twenty minutes later we eventually arrived. It was just off one of the main roads. A bumpy dirt track led to the nightspot, which looked like a big stone barrel. There was no large sign on the wall, no advertising – just the name 'Pufferbellies' written on a signpost along with other names on the roadside.

There was no lighting to lead you to the club. It was pitch dark. It resembled the club in Mexico from the film, *From Dusk Till Dawn*. It was a bit scary walking down the dark, deserted, dusty trail. Now was the time George Clooney would have been useful. We managed to arrive at the door without being attacked by blood sucking vampires, although we may have chosen them over the massive bouncers guarding the entrance. Now, they were scary. After thoroughly checking our passports, they strapped us with orange tags so we could go in and drink till we dropped.

It was close to ten when we strolled into the club. The cover charge was $10, and for underage citizens $15 – it would have to be good for this price. The place was very open and spacious. There were two pool tables as you walked in and a couple of arcade machines discreetly to one side. The first thing we did was to buy a couple of beers, as you do. The beers were sold in cans, unlike in Ireland where they came in pint glasses. These cans were also smaller than the ones back home. There were four diner-like seats along the wall that consisted of a wooden table and two padded benches either side. Then outside, 'Holy Shit', a volleyball court on a man-made beach. This had to be the coolest place going. Adjacent to this were five or six garden tables and chairs, with umbrellas covering them just in case of rain. At the moment they were proving their worth. There was a large area to the right of the volleyball court (wow!) with lots of tables and chairs. So obviously they expected the weather to pick up. In fairness, what nightclub would be complete without a hot dog stand. Jesus this place was sweet. There was a bar outside as well, and alongside that there was a smallish dance floor and a DJ box at the head of it.

Back inside, a staircase of about seven stairs led you up to a long mahogany bar and matching barstools. Here, you could enjoy a can while catching up with the latest goings-on in the sports world displayed on TV screens above your head. Beside the bar was the main dance area. There were mirrors all around the rectangular-shaped floor so you could cringe as you watched yourself attempt to dance. As the dance floor was situated a few feet above ground level, you had a panoramic view of the entire place – very useful if you were trying to find someone specific.

Above this, there was another floor. As before, seven steps brought you to the summit where there were another three pool tables, and the fourth and final bar was located here. Bingo, who was hanging out on this floor but the four American girls. Two of them in particular were like angels sent to the world in a moment of sheer brilliance – they were breathtaking. Introductions were made and we spent a few minutes getting to know them. The opportunity of being able to sit outside beside the volleyball court was too much for me. So the six of us rambled down the two staircases, passed the pool tables and out the open doors.

As we nattered away amongst ourselves, the girls looked a bit puzzled. They said to Michael and myself that we had drunk ten cans of beer. Looking down at the expanding collection of tinies I wondered what was so amazing about that. They told us that if they drank that amount, even a couple of beers, they would be jarred. We couldn't believe it; this was the real difference between our two cultures. If an Irish person, male or female, ever admitted that they could only drink two beers before they were locked, they would be unmercifully and universally slagged for the rest of the night or else thrown out of the pub. The only solution was that the girls would have to learn from us. We would be only too happy to teach them the 'way of the can'. There may well be vicious hangovers, and there could well be violent projectile vomiting, but with practise and persistence, we would raise their drinking capacity to a guaranteed four and a half cans.

In the end we were thrilled with the club. It had just about everything you could want, and more. For the lovers of hip-hop, outside was the place to be, while for fans of dance music, the inside dance floor would be your element. We had found the holy grail of nightclubs, and the fact that it was open every Sunday night was a great notch on Hyannis's bedpost. It would give us something to look forward to at the end of every week. Come the next morning, the anticipation of next Sunday night was already beginning to build.

After what turned out to be a fantastic night, the following morning continued in the same fashion. We had our first really nice day. The sun shone so brightly it was blinding. Our glasses would finally get the use for which they were intended. Today was a day for the beach.

J.F. Kennedy beach was a five-minute cycle from the motel. It was totally serene and viciously charming. Pearly-white boats were moored a couple of hundred yards offshore, and the ocean glistened under the noon sun. What a difference the sun makes to a place. We had no idea it could look so glorious when we toured the area in the lashing rain a few days ago. This was paradise.

As we cycled along the path, a puddle of sand lay inconspicuously on the ground. Not seeing this, Michael cycled straight into it. The bike came to an abrupt halt and Michael was tossed from Honey. In fairness to him it did look pretty cool as he flew through the air, similar to a paper plane. He landed on the ground gashing his hand on the corner of a rock, and just like that, blood started gushing from the palm of his hand.

One quick story before I carry on. About three months before we came away, Michael was thrown into a pond by a bodybuilder in Wexford. There were sharp rocks scattered around this particular pond and as he splashed into the water one of the rocks cut the palm of his hand. It was so deep you could actually see and touch the bone (it was quite smooth, according to Michael). Now it had happened to the exact same spot, but on the opposite hand.

Sunbathing a few metres away, three girls from the area came to Michael's rescue. They took pity on him and bandaged the wound with tissues. We ended up catching some rays with the girls for about two hours. They even rang a local restaurant to get them to deliver burgers and chips to us. I'm sorry to say this but thank you Michael for falling so theatrically off your bike, the food went down a treat.

That day at the beach we also met two girls from Cork. We hit it off from the start. They were friendly and outgoing and we talked for some time. Michael and myself were organising our first house, or should I say, room party, later that night so we invited the girls.

Michael and I decided to go out for a romantic meal together before the party. We settled on a Chinese restaurant at the start of Main Street. It was relatively cheap and plain – just what we wanted. We ordered chicken satay with rice, which would become a regular dish for us. A couple of glasses of wine were added to help wash it down. The Chinese waiter tiptoed over, trying his best not to spill any on the floor, and set them down within reaching distance.

'Me have ID.' The Oriental stated to us.

We looked at each other.

'Ah ye, fair play to ya, boy.'

He repeated his original sentence but this time pointed at us. A pre-dinner game of charades, brilliant, they didn't have this at home. After a few attempted guesses at the answer he finally managed to explain that he needed to see our IDs if we wanted wine. A sip or two had already been taken as we rattled our brains trying to think of the solution. Now, with our bellies lined we were ready for the social event of the night.

There was excitement in the air as party-time drew near. We were expecting a good turnout – we pretty much invited all the Irish we could tell. The girls from Fitchburg we met the night before were also coming so there would be no lack of entertainment.

People were starting to arrive early. Easily known we weren't in Ireland where people stroll through the door just as the party is coming to an end and the national anthem is beginning to play. There was plenty of space outside the room in the courtyard as there were very few cars. Every room had garden furniture outside the window, so people could sit and relax in the open air and have a drink or chat, whatever took their fancy. We borrowed (took without asking) a few tables and chairs. As folk were turning up, who should we see purposefully trudging over in our general direction, to no doubt voice some more obscure objections but the man himself, Mr Miagi.

He told us we would all have to move inside, that he wouldn't allow us to drink in the courtyard. We tried to reason with the guy and promised we would keep the music and the noise to a minimum. But he wouldn't budge. It would now have to be an inside party even though we were kind of limited for space. He stood in the courtyard shooing us into the room like dogs. When we were all safely tucked away out of sight, Mr Miagi stood at the entrance of the motel and refused entry to anyone else. Someone managed to slip past on the blind side and report back to us news of his actions. I went outside. Jessica and Clodagh, the two girls from Cork we had met earlier on the beach, were standing outside along with a few others. At this stage, Mr Miagi had gone back inside. This gave us the opportunity to sneak in. We were like soldiers crossing enemy lines.

The room was full. It resembled some sort of orgy; the beds were jammed and the floor was crowded. As we sat around sipping from our colourful metal cans it struck me that I was attracted to Jessica. She had a mysterious air about her, one that I couldn't quite figure out. In many respects she was intriguing. There seemed to be some sort of mutual connection between the pair of us. She was very attractive with piercing blue eyes and straight brown hair. We talked for a while and slowly got to know each other.

She told me about her nightmare journey coming across. She was meant to be flying with a few friends but when they reached London, the airline had managed to fuck up her booking for the outbound flight to America. They told her she'd either have to wait till the next day to fly to New York, or take a plane back to Cork. The airline weren't prepared to put her up in a hotel and she was advised against sleeping in the airport, as Heathrow is sometimes a bit dangerous at night. Taking this into account, she decided to fly back to Cork. She was extremely upset and immensely frustrated. The rest of her friends had already left for the States to begin their adventure, while she was sitting in the lobby waiting for a plane to take her back home.

While she was standing in the queue to board, a girl who worked behind the desk for her original airline came running up to her. Jessica was literally about to hand up her boarding pass, when she informed her that there was a seat available for her on the next flight to New York. A sigh of relief was audible, even though a niggling anger remained at the airline's bumble. She eventually got to America but had to face the prospect of being alone in New York at four in the morning with no place to stay. I think that would scare the bejesus out of any human being. Later that day she met up with Clodagh unscathed and still in one piece.

On reflection, we had been blessed with a pleasant and enjoyable trip over. Which is what everyone wants when they plan to go to the States for the summer, as it's the official start of your escapades. Despite been stuck in a living hell for a lot of her journey, Jessica was determined not to let it affect her summer.

The noise levels in the room had reached record highs. The neighbours would begin to complain soon so we had to stop the party. A few select people stayed and the rest left. The remainder went across the way to other rooms to balance things out. The girls from Fitchburg stayed along with Deco, one of the guys from Cork that was crashing in a room on the opposite side.

Deco was a mad bastard, full of the craic and always up for some spontaneous fun; the kind of guy you wanted and in many ways needed to make any party complete. With a passion for rollerblading and a physique conducive to it, Deco spent many an hour perfecting his already sharp technique at the blading track out by the ice-skating rink, which for obvious reasons was closed till November. He had left a girlfriend back home whom he was deeply in love with and vice versa. They both lived life to the full during the summer and made no wild promises of faithfulness when they were apart. They were realistic at the end of the day, and knew that whatever happened with other people, they would inevitably end up back together still crazy about one another in September. And wouldn't you know it, they were right.

In America, smoking weed is a popular pastime with people of all ages, especially young people – just as drinking is in Ireland. One of the girls brought some pot with her. She provided the joints and we provided the beer, a fair exchange of goods, I thought. As we were enjoying our mix of illegal substances, the joint went out. It was then passed to Deco. One of the girls asked him if he wanted a light.

'No I don't want a fuckin' light!'

She looked bewildered.

'Of course I want a fuckin' light!'

Ah, the famous sarcastic Irish quality, which the Americans couldn't fathom for love nor money. They didn't possess the same kind of sense of humour as us. A lot of the time our wit was completely lost on them. Sometimes it was like we were speaking a different language. They just didn't have a clue what we were talking about on occasions, which was very funny. When Deco made these comments to the girls I couldn't stop laughing. I was only just short of letting a stream of wee escape and run down my leg. It had to be one of the funniest remarks I heard that summer. The girls, however, didn't get the same kick out of it and, in the end, thought Deco was touched and must have been popping loony pills.

The next day the weather was back to its old tricks. We had seen what Hyannis could look like at its best so that gave us hope. We were in such a good mood from the last couple of days that we didn't care what the weather was doing. All our early worries concerning Hyannis had melted away over the weekend. We found out the kind of fun we could have here, and new friendships were being cemented at warp-speed. We had Pufferbellies to look forward to every Sunday along with the ever-increasing amount of parties that were beginning to spring up.

That night we were to suffer a major set back, a jolt to our mood. Michael and I sat outside the room enjoying a couple of beers. While Michael had gone to the jacks, Mr Miagi spotted me and came marching over like an officer in the Chinese army. He insisted that I'd have to go inside. This was getting a bit tedious. He would make an effective prison warden. Calmly and politely, I reminded him of what he had said only the previous night, that if there were three or four of us sitting outside he would allow it. In fact, right now, there was only me sitting outside. This didn't seem to matter to little Hitler as he ordered us into the room. When Michael had come back out we tried to plead our case but, instead, he rang the police – what a shit.

We stayed seated as two police squad cars rolled up. We felt we were doing nothing wrong so we stood our ground. One cop from each of the cars got out.

Everyone in the motel at the time, the Irish and the Americans, were mesmerized and watched the unfolding scene with great interest. The cops came over and asked what the story was. Mr Miagi started moaning and saying that he had asked us to go into the room and that we had refused. We told the police that Mr Miagi said we could sit outside if there weren't too many of us and we weren't making excessive noise. We didn't even have the radio on. The two cops asked to see our IDs. They seemed sympathetic towards our cause but said if Mr Miagi wanted us inside we would have to cooperate. Mr Miagi then dropped a bombshell, stating that he was throwing us out in the morning, and turning to the officers said.

'Put in police diary, they go out tomorrow.'

It was comical. The two cops just stood there staring at him as if he was a few grains of fried rice short of a portion. Well, that would be our last night in the Best Value Inn and would top off a very eventful first week.

4

Mr Miagi, you rat you

There was a heavy, awkward silence as we packed our bags the next morning. Emma and Alyssa were upset at being chucked out of our familiar quarters in the Best Value Inn. They were worried about where we were going to live. A week had gone and we weren't any closer to finding somewhere we could call home. We had sort of stopped searching any further once we had become comfortable in the motel. The reality of it was until we found long-term accommodation we couldn't really unpack or settle into a place properly. Guys don't really mind this minor inconvenience as we can very easily live out of a suitcase or a backpack. But the two girls were pissed off. Michael and myself did our best to try and reassure them that we'd find a place sooner rather than later and encouraged them to stay positive.

With a two finger farewell to Mr Miagi and his fat sons, we were away. The taxi brought us, and all our paraphernalia to the Econo Lodge Motel. With a name like that we weren't expecting the Hilton – more like a cockroach-infested, battered old building that served you gruel instead of bagels every morning. It was located about five minutes cycle from Main Street. The rooms were, again, located around the back of the building. It was nothing special, a bit shitty-looking actually, but we had arrived with no grand illusions.

Again, just like the Best Value Inn, it was owned and run by foreigners, this time, Packies. But there was one advantage – the rooms had fridges. Cold beer, we had moved up in the world. Once we had hauled our suitcases up two flights of stairs, it was time for a cold drink. I put our mascot up on the shelf – a shiny new sports hubcap that Michael had brought back as a present for me one night when he and Emma were out for a meal. Where he got it I'll never know, but it did look good on the shelf. We also emptied out the towels, pillows and Bible that we robbed from the Best Value Inn – I know it was petty but it felt good.

That night we decided to throw a bit of a beach party to cheer ourselves up. Some good company and a few pitchers should do the trick. We spread the word and stocked up on drink from the liquor store. The festivities began early in the Best Value. We had to keep quiet with only a select few in the rooms otherwise the Triads would get suspicious. We left the motel at about 10.30. The beach was a fifteen-minute walk away. Not a lot, but when you're carrying a big bunch of cans in a plastic bag that could burst at any time, it's a long drag. I'd say every car that passed us on the road must have been saying to themselves, 'oh look, the Irish are back.' What other race would have the cheek to saunter down the road at eleven at night heading for the beach to get pie-eyed.

There were about twenty of us altogether at our beach soiree. Jessica and Clodagh joined us, as they only lived across the road. We found a spot that was hopefully out of earshot and the watchful eye of the police. We made use of the big boulders that split the beach in two. On one side there was water and on the other dry ground. It was perfect. The night was cold but the rain had stopped. Apart from the moonlight, darkness engulfed us. Some of the Cork boys had bought a CD player from one of the cheap bargain stores. It set them back $30, which they split between them. It was easier than lugging one all the way from Ireland with the very real risk of it being damaged or robbed by a music-loving hippie.

It was a change to have a party on the beach. Back home we were used to having parties every other way and in every possible place except the beach. The normally shitty weather usually deters us from partaking in this original pastime. All snuggled up on the rocks, being kept warm by the body heat of the person next to you, listening to the profound words coming from the talented lungs of Bono, and drinking Busch Light under the pale moon sky. What more could a person ask for.

This particular night, I had more than that. I had a girl sitting beside me who I really liked and we seemed to be hitting it off well. It was so easy, like we had known each other for years instead of days. Jessica sat beside me on the massive boulder we were using as our own personal couch. The conversation flowed between us as we began to get closer. To me, it seemed like no one else was there, just the two of us and the soothing melody of U2 in the background.

After a while Jessica started to shiver from the cold. I accompanied her back to her house so she could get a coat. You had to cross the beach and a couple of small fields to get there. Once she was wrapped up snug we made our way back via the scenic route. Before you came to the actual beach itself, there was a small commemorative area overlooking the ocean. There was a large wall that had a plaque on it honouring the people who died in one of the wars when J.F. Kennedy was in power. It was tastefully surrounded by immaculately trimmed bushes and plants. Encompassing this were a number of stone benches, and in the middle, lay a fountain.

The both of us laughed and chatted together. We sat on the stone benches, which weren't exactly velvety, but we didn't care. There was an undisputable atmosphere between us – a chemistry you could literally feel. We kissed. It felt as natural as breathing. It was a special moment as we sat beside the lyrical hums of the singing fountain alone under the moonlight in Cape Cod. I couldn't think of a more romantic setting or a nicer girl to experience my first kiss with in America. This really was turning into a memorable night.

Luckily enough, we managed to escape the attentions of the police, and see the party through till the small hours without being arrested for public disorder. Everyone seemed to thoroughly enjoy their first beach experience. For some, it helped to forge new friendships. For me, it may have helped me find a summer romance or even something more. Hopefully when the weather improved, we would have the chance to bask in the enjoyable surroundings of many more of these highly entertaining ocean-side retreats.

A couple of days had passed since we had started applying for jobs. Now was the time to follow them up and try to nail one. We called back to every restaurant and bar we had applied to. Surprisingly, everywhere told us that either they had no positions available or they would have openings in a couple of weeks' time when the tourist season kicked in. It wasn't the sort of response we were expecting. Places like Chillies, Pizzeria Uno and other chained restaurants you would imagine would be looking for staff, weren't. The independent restaurants took the same line as well as all the bars on Main Street. Neither was there work as dockhands on the boats and ferries. We tried a few of the hotels in the area, including the Sheraton, which had told us to call back. But these, too, seemed indifferent to the thought of giving us jobs. The sound of the word 'no' was becoming very tiresome and the more we heard it the more irritated we became.

We had gone up to the local golf course a few days beforehand. I wanted to find out about caddying and Michael thought he could try the restaurant. He went inside while I made my way down to the clubhouse to check things out. To his annoyance, once again, that little bloody word flew from someone's mouth quashing his hopes of becoming a waiter. I talked to the guy in the pro shop and he said there was a meeting about caddying in four days' time. That wasn't too bad. I could easily make my $200 stretch that far if I needed to.

While we were there, four middle-aged golfers had just shaken hands and walked off the eighteenth green. Being polite we said hello to them. Once they caught the accent they knew we were Irish and started chatting to us. During the conversation we told them that we were busy looking for jobs but hadn't had any luck so far. One of them said the guy they were playing with (who was currently packing his clubs neatly into the boot of his car) owned the Cape Codder Resort. We had seen this place on our way into town on the day we arrived in Hyannis.

We were brought over and introduced to Frank. Frank was an Italian-American and seemed nice enough. He instructed us to pop by the Cape Codder during the week and ask for one of two managers. Now we were getting places, and to make things even better, one of the people we were to see was from Ireland. This was it, we thought. This was our chance. We had made our faces known by getting out there and networking and had managed to secure an important contact that, hopefully, could do us a favour. All this hard work and constant rejection would be worth it in the end. We were sure of that.

Meanwhile, Emma, Laoibhse and Maria had managed to land jobs. Before they came over they applied for waitressing positions on the Internet in a restaurant called the 'Duck Inn'. Strangely enough the guy who owned it was the original owner of the Best Value Inn. It was a real pity he had sold it to the Miagi's. Despite having these jobs the shifts were few and far between. With the tourist season yet to take off there was a scarcity of people and of work. They spent the majority of the time not in work or else being told to go home because rigor mortis was setting in.

Jessica and myself were becoming closer as the days went by. Michael and I were regular visitors to her and Clodagh's house. The girls were like us in that they spent a lot of their time together and would rarely be seen on their own. Clodagh was a lovely, friendly girl who didn't possess any sort of malice or desire to hurt. She had a pleasant, welcoming nature with a soft voice and had absolutely no qualms about making friends with just about everyone she met. Jessica and herself were well matched and they would have no difficulty living in each other's pockets for three months.

The house was a gem.

Every time I went inside I couldn't help but be impressed with their delightful summer home. They had it all to themselves. It had two bathrooms, a nice kitchen with all the fundamental appliances, including a big fridge to house the alcoholic refreshments and a cooker for their everyday nutritional needs. They had a good-sized bedroom between them. But they had no beds and had to make do with some yellow foam stuff and a few blankets (however, later on in the summer they were given two single beds by their landlady). They also had their own washing facilities around the back of the house which was a major perk because we had to spend our time running to the launderette every few days with our dirty clothes. There was a basement, too, which had a double bed, but it was cold at night so they chose to stay in the upstairs room instead.

A friend of theirs attending college in Scotland was expected over shortly. She was also dragging a girl she befriended there along for the ride. They would be given the basement room.

Early romances were beginning to develop like wildfire back in the Best Value Inn. I was surprised Mr Miagi didn't put a ban on all non-platonic relationships because he feared potential guests might get the wrong idea as to the nature of his motel. Maria hooked up with one of the Cork boys, Bono. He was one of the guys sharing the room with Nevaeh and Clare. Bono was an all-round nice guy who didn't have a bad bone in his body. It was clear that Maria really fancied him because she described him as a pot of sauce – a term of endearment kept for only the best looking of guys. They made an attractive couple. Their outgoing personalities and easy-going natures blended together perfectly. From the start you could see the potential of this pairing.

Another blossoming romance occurred between Jacob and Shauna – another inter-county match. Desperate to be alone they often snuck into different rooms locking doors behind them so they could have some quality time together. They were an intense couple who couldn't seem to get enough of each other, and when they were apart, they felt alone.

It can be very hard to keep a lid on all those pent-up passions. These two couldn't quite hold in their urges and desires while Maria and Bono managed to be a bit more discreet about their affections for each other. The traditional rivalry between Dublin and Cork seemed a long way away from here. Whoever said Dublin was too good for Cork and Cork too good for Dublin? Whoever it was could certainly do with strapping on a white coat and getting a reality check in their local clinic.

While this was all nice and rosy, other people weren't so fortunate. Michael and Emma, who had been going out for a little over two and a half years, were starting to feel the pinch on their relationship early on. They had been warned by many that spending the summer in America together would either make or break them.

It's tough keeping close to one another when you're away like this, especially as the level of freedom is something you would never have experienced back home. It's not a normal life. It feels like you're in a daydream because it's so completely different than at home in Ireland. The urge to go mad and try new things and experience different situations is immense. Most people only get one stab at living in America so they feel compelled to do everything under the sun, both the good and the bad, in order to make the most of their summer and have the best possible time they can. This is why relationships can be susceptible to potential long-term damage. It takes huge effort on both sides to keep the relationship alive and hold on to the bond that was there before you both left, making sure it's as strong when you're ready to leave.

It wasn't surprising that Michael and Emma were going through a rough patch, even though they were always a close couple, a couple you would offer favourable odds to succeed. They were mad about each other, and it would take something very drastic to separate them. From the beginning of the holiday Michael and myself joined forces and we became virtually inseparable. We practically did everything together, from exploring Hyannis to meeting and making friends with new people. We were like Butch Cassidy and the Sundance Kid or the Bushwhackers from WWF of old. The fact that Emma had her friends and Michael had only me as his sole male companion, it meant that the pair of us ended up spending the bulk of our time together.

They saw very little of each other during the first couple of weeks and this made Emma slightly frustrated. She would have preferred to spend more time with him, which was totally understandable. No doubt they had made plans about what they would do when they came to the States, but for the moment, things weren't going as anticipated.

Most of the week, the weather had been atrocious. That one day of glorious sunshine we had last week, when everyone got burnt, was a flash in the pan. I wouldn't say Clare was too bothered though, the sun damaged her so much that her face came out in scarlet-red blisters and her body was racked by pain – she was just happy to see the back of sunlight for a while. The rain poured down without any regard for the season. It matched my mood; I was going through a bit of low. I had no job, no house and the weather wasn't helping.

There was very little in the way of entertainment when it was raining and it wasn't as if we had the money to spend on a day out to help keep us occupied. It sucked the energy out of you and replaced it instead with bad forms. Anything would have been better than sitting around becoming lethargic. The monotony was like a death sentence hanging over us. For some unknown reason nobody could get a job. We had a theory that there was some sort of shady conspiracy aimed at the Irish. When we went to the social security office the day we arrived, the security guard said we would have no problem finding a job. He would no doubt be eating his hat (once he removed the cream puff) if we paid him a little visit now, but the incessant rain was stopping us from doing even that.

Yet there would be light at the end of the dark tunnel. One evening we went to visit the girls in the Best Value Inn – I should just call it the Concentration Camp Inn. Maria told us that her boss was looking for three strong, capable guys to help clear out a basement on Saturday morning. This didn't describe us but we thought we'd give it a shot anyway. She said it could lead to a few days' work. Class, just what we needed to alleviate our mental anxieties. It would also be a welcome return to solvency as money was running out fast.

I decided to open a bank account that second week, it might help me to stop spending money foolishly on things I didn't need (don't worry beer I don't mean you). After checking out a couple of banks I finally found the perfect one, right in the middle of Main Street. The other banks I tried wanted $600 put in their sweaty hands before one could open an account, which for yours truly was impossible. They also charged a hefty fee when you closed your account which I also knew I wouldn't be able to afford.

The Rockland Trust was a quaint little bank. It felt more like a home than a bank, which was refreshing. They required only $400 to become a saver with them, which I didn't have but which Michael lent me. I took this back out straightaway and returned it to him before the food court began chanting my name. They also did you the courtesy of not taking your hard earned cash when you parted with them at the end of the summer. The main attraction of this bank, however, was the baskets of free lollypops that were strategically placed on all the countertops. These baskets often provided enough empty calories to keep me going for a couple of hours. The staff was friendly and open. From the start I had a healthy relationship with them, which was always beneficial if you had to get on bended knee and beg for more money.

There was a girl working there for the season being trained in by a fellow female employee who was bonkers but great craic. The girl, I later learned, was a Mormon. I discovered this one night in the Blue Room from one of her male colleagues as he spluttered over his words after one too many beers. In case you don't know what a Mormon is, as I didn't at the time, it's a person who lives life by a very strict code. They don't drink, smoke or engage in any activity that may be seen as immoral or bad for you. The majority of the Mormons in America live in Utah.

This particular girl was twenty-three (coincidentally she had the same date of birth as I do) and was already married and had settled down for good. Somehow I wouldn't say this rigid regime would work back home, and I definitely couldn't see Michael standing in line to sign up. When you think of all the different types of people that make up the US, it is truly a highly diverse land.

I applied for an ATM card, which could be used at night when I needed something to quench my thirst after eating a few too many ten-cent chocolate mints from the liquor shop. This took the best part of a week to be delivered.

I was to be out of action for a few days during the middle of the week. A feckin' flu got its green, germ-ridden claws into me and I felt like asking for a lethal injection to put me out of my misery. I took to the bed and hoped for a quick recovery. When you have a change of climate you become very vulnerable to foreign bacteria and bugs that may cause colds and flu's. I'm not sure why I got it, the climate on the Cape was the exact same as at home. I could think of only one good thing to come from my illness, I wouldn't be able to spend anymore of my rapidly diminishing money. I was fortunate in some ways because I had about as much money left as a tramp on the street after a day's begging.

While I was out of commission, condemned to my sick bed, a beach party was organised. There were about twenty five or so people at it. While it was taking place a number of cops realised what was going on and went down to investigate. They must have seen them with their spotlights as they patrolled the nearby area. They asked everyone if they were over twenty-one and nobody made a comment. They then said.

'Some of you guys must be over twenty-one.'

Three people raised their hands. Even if everybody had have been over twenty-one, it was still illegal to drink in a public place. To everyone's astonishment, the cops let it go and left them there to get on with their drinking, asking only for the place to be cleaned up in return. I think over the years the police had come to terms with the Irish and their ways and were prepared to give us some latitude concerning drinking and parties. They knew we were legally able to drink at home and didn't mind turning the other cheek as long as we, in turn, respected the place.

Once I was on the road to recovery, Michael and myself headed off to the Cape Codder Resort Hotel to seek jobs. It took about fifteen minutes to get there by bike. It was extremely humid that day and we looked like drowned rats as we walked into the Hearth And Kettle Restaurant, which was part of the resort. It was a lovely romantic setting – old-fashioned and cosy with its wooden floors and inviting fireplace. We asked to speak to the Irish manager we were advised to see. He told us to call back in a week's time, as they'd probably have some vacancies then. Terrific, we had been sent on another wild goose chase. At least we had work for the morning clearing out the basement and, if we were lucky, it might lead to bigger and better things.

That night, we stayed well away from the potent juice. Well we just had a couple because we had to meet Richard, the guy we were to be working for, outside the Best Value Inn at eight in the morning. We wanted to be energetic and enthusiastic (well, as enthusiastic as you could be at the thought of cleaning out a basement).

The next morning we were only too happy to be up and out of bed by seven. We finally had work for ourselves after two weeks of searching high and low about Hyannis. We were there before eight so as to give the impression we were serious about our new job and hoping to earn some extra brownie points. Richard turned up a few minutes later and asked if we were ready to start. We were then informed (get this) that we would be clearing out the basement of the Best Value Inn. Oh holy fuck. This could only happen to us. Bugger it, we'd do it, it was work after all and we needed the money. We were given our instructions and left to it. There was a mountain of carpets that we had to lug from the basement, up the stairs, and outside onto the grass. Working with us was one of the guys from Cork who lived here. He was a member of the gang we had formed.

This was Al's third year in Hyannis. Though, he wasn't technically going to be over for the entire summer. He had worked all year and saved a good few quid. It was more like a long holiday. He hadn't planned on getting a full-time job and he was only doing this because Maria had asked him if he could help us out for the morning.

The basement was horrible. It had a big noisy boiler that was trying its best to deafen us, and long pipes ran the length of the floor. There was a huge black dude working on the boiler wearing a pair of overalls. He was gigantic and was the spit and image of the prisoner from the film, *The Green Mile*. He was jolly, like a big black Santa Claus – that sort of personality. We got to work carting out the carpets. They were dusty and old and the smell wasn't pretty. What we would have given for a couple of Glade Plug-ins to neutralise the musty odour. We had Mr Miagi and one of his relations, who looked like your typical villain from a Chinese gangland movie, watching our every move like hawks and barking out instructions we could hardly understand – just like when we stayed there. This time we were actually working for him and he was in control of us.

When we cleared out the first load of rugs, we uncovered a whole new batch, which were twice the size and twice the weight of their predecessors. Until now I never realised carpets could be some bloody heavy. It took two of us to lift one of the oversized fuckers. This put us at a disadvantage. As we only numbered three, one of us was always standing around like a spare prick at a wedding. It was backbreaking, and because the carpets unravelled and expanded a little bit, this made our job all the more awkward. We had to carry the carpets up a steep flight of stairs that happened to have a low roof. We banged our heads continuously. I felt sorry for Al. He was taller than us and ultimately suffered the worst. We were hunched over all the time, as it wasn't possible to carry them correctly with the staircase we had to negotiate.

We hauled down one of the carpets from the big pile and discovered a dead, decayed rat underneath it. They expected us to handle diseased rodents for a measly $8 an hour. It is well known that rats carry diseases and who knows what you could catch off dead ones. We scrambled upstairs to find Mr Miagi to tell him we weren't going to work in those sorts of conditions. He came down to see for himself what we were working in. Examining the rat.

'This is not rat, just dust.'

Well that's the funniest looking dust we've ever seen, we told him. It must have had a life of its own and formed itself into the shape of a rat. We told him we weren't working anymore and that was that. Al told Mr Miagi that he did environmental science in college and started listing off all the possible diseases you could contract from being in contact with rats. All bullshit of course but Mr Miagi knew no better. He could have said it was possible to catch Spotted Dickitus and Mr Miagi wouldn't have been any the wiser.

Mr Miagi told us to wait while he rang Richard. Five minutes later Richard was standing over the stash of mildewed carpets inspecting the rat. We voiced our objections and told him we couldn't stay here anymore for the sake of our health. He made a comment, which still makes me angry whenever I think of it. He looked at the three of us.

'Come on, I thought you guys were Irish.'

What a pompous prick. Someone should tell him we weren't living in the early twentieth century anymore and that Irish people weren't slaves, especially not his. I could have floored him for that remark. I decided against it. I needed the $16 we were owed for the two hours' work. The money was to be put to a good cause by buying much needed life-saving hydration (a full case of Busch Light), and vital nourishment (lunch in McDonalds). At least we had something to show for our blackened clothes and bent spines.

Four days had gone, just like that. That's the length of time we had originally booked ourselves into the Econo Lodge Motel for and we still weren't any closer to finding a proper place to live. We had viewed a basement a couple of days ago. It was big for a basement but the landlord lived upstairs and the rent was unreasonably high – another dead end. We decided to stay for another four nights. It was nicer than the Best Value Inn and wasn't run by a nazi dictator, but it was too far out of the way. We wanted to be closer to Main Street and closer to all the lads. We hoped and prayed that we could find somewhere better in the days to come. All we wanted was a place that didn't have the landlords living there. Surely that wasn't too much to ask.

Meanwhile, we continued looking for jobs and fortune was to come our way in the angelic form of Nevaeh. Cycling down Main Street one evening we bumped into Clare and herself as they sat outside the games arcade on a bench, eagerly tucking into some ice cream. We told them about our struggle to find employment. Out of nowhere, Nevaeh said the arcade were looking for a couple of guys to do some manual work. Sitting there calmly eating her vanilla ice cream, I wondered how she knew this – she must have been our guardian angel sent to get us jobs. We also found out that Clare had been threatened with deportation after not checking in with Sevis to inform them of her whereabouts. She managed to log on before the FBI sent out the headhunters thinking she was an international terrorist who was about to blow-up America.

In two seconds flat we were at the information booth in the arcade asking the girl from Limerick, who worked there, about the job that was on offer. She got the manager who told us to be at the arcade in a couple of days' time, at eight in the morning. Our job would be to help put up bouncing castles two days a week for the twice-weekly festivals that took place along Main Street during the summer. He would pay us $100 each for each day worked.

What a find. Nevaeh officially became our best friend, taking the reins from Maria who had dropped to the bottom of the pile after getting us the once in a lifetime opportunity of going rat spotting. We could now afford to relax a bit and not worry so much about our financial woes.

Back in the Best Value Inn people were starting to get sick of the constant lectures and threats being dished out by Mr Miagi and his sons. They watched every move and were quick to offer ear bashings from hell, or China even. It was like living in jail.

Three guys from Cork, who were over together, were the next in line to be evicted from the Best Value household. What was once a place of unity with a fun-filled environment was now turning into a living nightmare. Nobody could sneeze without being watched and judged. You could see the powers that be wondering if illegal snuff had been responsible for the snotty outburst. The management seemed to be trying their best to get the Irish to move out. I couldn't understand this. They were making $380 a week from each room we took, and it's not as if we were destroying the place or setting fire to it. Thinking back now, maybe we should have. The motel was half empty and we made up most of their client base. So you'd imagine they would try and treat us with a bit of respect and dignity instead of making every effort to encourage us to leave.

They were like the Chinese Triads, a whole litter of them tracing your every move. It wouldn't surprise me if they installed miniature cameras in every room just to complete the Big Brother scenario that already existed. It may even have made a prime-time show on Fox.

One afternoon, a few of us were engaging in a spot of sunbathing on the beach. After about an hour or so of this most relaxing pursuit, I had to stop. It was about all I could take before I turned into glowing amber. As I was on my way over to see Jessica, I ran into Nevaeh crossing the J.F.K Memorial Ground. We ended up becoming engrossed in conversation. I had totally forgotten my prior arrangement to meet Jessica – she probably thought I died of sunstroke or had a heart attack when I saw how burnt I was.

We talked of life – our ups and downs, our present situations, days gone by, and of things that really mattered. It was an unexpected talk, open and honest, meaningful and heart-warming. We didn't know each other that well. Yet from the start there seemed to be an almost spiritual connection between us that, strangely, allowed us to tell each other our most personal secrets.

She told me of her break up with her boyfriend just before she left, and I told her about my split with my girlfriend nine months previous. I was surprised to hear of her suffering from loneliness and depression when she told me. She had always appeared to be so confident and happy and fun loving. But feelings are often hidden deep down concealed from the judging eyes of the world. Sometimes it can be so well hidden on the face of that person that you may never know the truth, especially if they choose never to let you into the deepest, darkest parts of their soul. It can be lonely keeping all that emotion bottled-up inside. A lot of the time it eats through your very being, and the only way to set yourself free is by sharing your feelings with someone you can really trust. I was honoured and flattered that Nevaeh felt she could let me into a part of her that very few people would ever see.

I told her about my emotional roller coaster of a year, and how I yearned to get away from the trials and tribulations of life back home. This summer acted as a blissful escape from reality. A chance to learn about myself, to discover what I wanted and to try and get back to how I once felt before last year ever happened. It would help me to get my life and feelings into perspective. Hopefully, if I was lucky enough, it would give me a few hints on coping with the difficulties that lay ahead, and maybe answers to some important questions. I told her of my desire to have a fantastic, unforgettable three months, to clear my head of all the worries that had plagued it and to make as many great friends as I could.

It was safe to say from that day on, things got better. Nevaeh became radiant; she was like a dazzling bright light on the Cape. She became a happier person inside and out, and a special friend to a lot of people, including myself.

Jack finally arrived over. He was the most easy-going guy you could ever meet and always seemed to have a smile on his broad, friendly face. Born in the county of Longford, he was very down to earth and as easy to talk to as one of your own family. Jack had passed his third year in college but failed to get the required mark to progress through to the next year. He didn't seem overly worried or upset about this. He was just happy to be in America and intended to make the most of it.

With Jack's arrival I was relegated to a pull-up bed on the floor. The two couples retained possession of the double beds. The only real disadvantage to this was the risk of been stood on in the middle of the night as someone, half asleep and still drunk, clumsily attempted to make their way to the toilet. Before leaving home I was aware that it wasn't going to be a walk in the park and that sometimes I would have to sleep in some weird and unusual places. It didn't bother me in the slightest. I was ready for anything.

The next night I was to have a different sleeping arrangement. I was bunking in with two delightful young girls, Jessica and Clodagh. I was looking forward to sleeping on some spongy, yellow foam – I hadn't tried that yet. After consuming a few jars with the lads back in the motel room I was ready to hit the girls' house. I must have got there at about half eleven. The three of us were enjoying a drink when out of nowhere, a trio of American guys appeared. Jessica and Clodagh's friends had arrived over a couple of days ago, and her Scottish friend, Rebecca, had taken a liking to one of the Americans.

I had learned a lot about American guys in the short time I had been in Hyannis, acquired in the different nightclubs I had been to, but also on the streets, in restaurants and every other place. I'm not trying to generalise here but they were all sleazy worms. I certainly wasn't the only one holding this opinion; most of the Irish I had talked to had similar views.

The guys would use every corny chat-up line in the book to score (the ones we joke about using, they use for real). They would pay false compliments to try and succeed in their pulling missions. Even if these tactics failed (as was the case most times) and they were turned down, they would hang around like an unwanted snot that clung to your nose. They didn't understand the meaning of 'no', and never knew when to call it a day and leave the poor girl alone. Sometimes this rejection would provoke feelings of revenge or hatred for the person who refused their advances.

How intimidating it must be for the girls who are continuously hounded by these filthy fornicators. I knew a few Irish girls who were tormented by some of these guys and they weren't impressed one bit, and who could blame them. Personally, I got very annoyed and protective when I saw this happening. Even if I didn't know the lass I couldn't help becoming aggravated with the constant harassment. Many of them were the kind of people who wouldn't hesitate in taking advantage or forcing themselves on a girl who had turned them down or denied them what they wanted.

From the start I didn't like the look of the three guys who were now sitting in Jessica's kitchen. For a normally chatty individual I went quiet, while they talked to the girls. Two o'clock slowly came and went. Jessica, Clodagh and their other friend Ann Marie were tired and wanted to go to bed. Good, I thought, some peace from the three stooges who couldn't hold their drink. We went into the bedroom while Ann Marie went down to the basement to bed. Rebecca and the guys stayed in the kitchen drinking and blabbering. The only problem was the more the Americans drank the louder and rowdier they became.

The neighbours upstairs put their foot down and began banging on the floor to get them to shut up. Jessica went into the kitchen and told them to go down to the basement where they would neither disturb the neighbours nor us. Ann Marie found it impossible to sleep with them down there so she came up to our room. About ten minutes later, just to check on things, Jessica went downstairs. Shocked and disgusted by what she saw she told them to come back up. The four of them were on the bed. One of them was lying on top of Rebecca while another one of the guys stroked her hair. I asked Jessica if she wanted me to ask them to leave but she said no because Rebecca would have flown off the hook. The fact was Rebecca was half scuttered anyway and probably didn't know what she wanted, which may have left her vulnerable to these pricks.

Four in the morning, and at this stage we were all knackered and fantasising about snoozing on flat yellow foam. I was getting more and more frustrated with every minute that went by. I decided to take a stand and told the girls I was going to get them to leave. They were loud and very much unwelcome. The two girls weren't happy with my decision. They believed Rebecca would go ape shit if I made them leave. But to be honest, I didn't give a flying fuck.

I walked into the kitchen and asked them to go because it was late and everyone wanted to get some sleep. A silence descended on the room. They looked at me as if to say, 'you have no right to be asking us to leave, you fucking leprechaun'. Reluctantly, they slowly made their way to the door and out. Feeling relieved, I went back into the room. The girls were happy they were gone, even if they didn't agree with what I had done. At last, we could all get some much-needed kip. Unfortunately, the three amadàns didn't see it like this. A couple of minutes after they left, one of them shouted in:

'Hey Beau, can you suck your own dick?'

All I heard of this half drunken inquiry was my name followed by dick. The girls didn't catch it either so I went out to find the missing part of the question. I asked the guy who was standing at the front door, waiting for me, what he had shouted in. He repeated what he had said. I was tired and suffering with quite a healthy rage. I dared him to ask me the question one more time, just for the record, in case I hadn't heard it properly. I didn't give a shit if there were three of them. My blood pressure was sky-high and I would have gone through a brick wall with each of them standing in front of it – with no helmet. Backing down he put his hand up.

'Don't talk to me man, just don't talk to me.'

With that, he and the other two losers walked away. They must have known we wanted to go to bed and being polite respected our wishes.

That Saturday morning we were expected at the amusement park to report for work at eight. This would be our first decent paycheque since we had come to the Cape. Michael and I were up on the stroke of seven so we could chill out and have a relaxing breakfast to set us up for the day ahead. We left the motel at 7.55. The park was only a couple of minutes cycle away. Our new boss said he would be there from half seven until a quarter past eight and warned us not to be late – point taken chief! We made it to the park at 8.01 and there was no sign of anyone; the place was deserted. No evidence of any bouncing castles existed. We waited on the bench outside for an hour and a half and he didn't show. This was bollocks; jobs just didn't seem keen on allowing us to handle them.

Later that day we called back to the park to find out what went wrong. We told him that we were there at a minute past eight and the place was empty. He countered by claiming to have been at the park till about five past and there was no sign of us. There was no point trying to argue, he wasn't having any of it. He told us we had lost our chance, and that was it. I think to this day that he fucked us over; he probably had second thoughts hiring us and tried to wriggle out of employing a pair of Irish guys by shifting the blame. The pair of us were fuming but we left it at that. Punching the guy would have only caused us trouble, and besides, we didn't have enough money to pay for bail. Another failed avenue. What did we have to do to get a proper job?

I kept the faith through all this bullshit and rejection. I had a caddy meeting to attend and hoped that this would lead to a permanent job and a regular income. I had budgeted my final $200 by drinking cheap beer and eating McDonalds – not too beneficial if you're trying to keep trim. It was about two thirds of the way into June, and times were starting to get hard.

Approximately ten other people huddled outside the pro-shop waiting for the meeting to begin. They were no older than fourteen or fifteen, mostly younger for that matter. I seemed to be the only Irish person there. I had thought there might be a few of us. The meeting was chaired by the head-pro at the club. He seemed to love himself a bit too much and was overly friendly to the extent of being fake. He told us the rules and regulations of being a caddy, how we should act on the course, and what places were off-limits. As it happened, we caddies were prohibited from entering anywhere, except the little caddyshack, which was made of wood, had one bench and was hidden from the golfers' view. Besides, what upstanding, posh golfer would want to look at a load of second-class citizens who merely acted as people's bag carriers.

Valued employees we were not.

As he went on, we were instructed that in order to be eligible to caddy, you would have to attend three training sessions. Ah fuck that, I thought, it wasn't a feckin' science. Yet, there was a bigger blow to follow because the next words that came out of his mouth were to be felt below the belt, and even more so in the pocket: the caddy season didn't begin until the July 4th weekend. BOLLOCKS! SHITE! GRASSHOLE! FECK-ARSE INDUSTRIES! HAIRY JAPANESE BASTARDS! MOTHER-FUCKIN' ARSE-BUISCUITS! I whispered aggressively under my breath. That was another twelve days away, how the hell could I survive till then? I would have to start eating grass from the fairways in order to obtain the essential vitamins and minerals my body needed, just like cows.

Back in the Best Value Inn (don't fall for the catchy name) things were rapidly going downhill. Mr Miagi was making people wish they had never been born (only a very slight exaggeration). He had also kindly decided to raise the rent to $500 a week for each room. I think he was suffering from some sort of narcissistic disillusionment. This was a crappy third-rate motel that didn't even have fridges in the rooms. It wasn't exactly the Ritz Plaza. People just weren't prepared to pay that sort of money for the service they were getting. Everyday one or two groups were upping and leaving this hellhole for greener pastures.

The Hyannis Travel Inn had become the new Irish sanctuary. Being stuck out in the Econo Lodge in Yarmouth, we found out about the migration to the Travel Inn a day or two later. That evening we went to visit some of the lads that had moved there. It was a genuinely lovely motel, much more superior than the last. Located just behind Main Street, a few paces from Hooters, it was in the perfect location. It had a clean and usable outdoor pool along with an indoor pool, sauna and hot tub. The rooms even had fridges. Holy armchair, Batman! This place was a world apart. You could even call it, motel heaven.

The new occupants had nothing but good things to say about the motel. Once again you could feel the happy atmosphere beginning to return. This was it; our time in the Econo Lodge was about to come to a thankful end the next day and this, it was agreed, was where we would come. Maybe our luck was beginning to change for the better. One thing was certain, though, we were definitely willing to find out.

5

Ladderman and
sidekicks go to town

For the second time of asking we were packing our bags to move to yet another motel. This was to be our third in all and would hopefully be more successful than the last couple. Just like the previous occasions the sky spit rain as we loaded our gear into the taxi. It was perhaps fortuitous that we were Irish because I don't think any other race could tolerate the amount of rain we were having. A short trip for the two girls and Jack, and bike ride for Michael and myself, and we had arrived at our new home for at least the next two weeks.

After checking into our room, which was more than adequate, we had the luxury of unpacking our cases. In the Econo Lodge this was impossible as we were only there for four days each time and had no idea when we would up and leave. It was such a great feeling to be settled in the one place and have everything put away and to know that you were staying there for a substantial period of time. Living out of a suitcase becomes a nuisance after a while; the traveller lifestyle isn't that glamorous. The girls in particular were glad of the new arrangements as they now had a place for their hair straightners, which was a relief. The rooms were spacious and informal and included the most important item of all, a beer-cooler or fridge, as it is more commonly known in civilised areas.

The next Pufferbellies beckoned us once again. We had learned from our mistake the previous week and, on the Saturday, we bought enough drink to keep us going. Unless you went to a pub or nightclub it was impossible to buy alcohol on a Sunday. All the liquor stores were closed and the normal shops that happened to sell alcohol would erect signs and barriers around that particular section. This was probably the single most annoying law in America, with nightclubs closing at one in the morning a close second.

Our new Sunday evening ritual would be strictly enforced each week – drinking from half seven, then cycling half pissed, high on life to the club for about half ten. Michael would buy a two-litre bottle of coke, fill it half full with vodka – the remainder being coke – and take it with him. We would have a few mouthfuls before we went in and then hide it underneath a big branch, which covered a hole in the ground around the side of the front door. The bottle was never discovered and was always there, loyally waiting for us when the night was over – you're the man, bottle.

The drinking had worked up quite a hunger so we decided to get a quick bite before hitting the club. There was nothing open as most of the restaurants closed early on the Cape. We had missed Burger King by a few minutes but the drive-thru was still serving. Arriving at the intercom, the shrill voice of a bored Burger King worker asked us what we'd like and we started to order. Promptly, she then said that we didn't qualify as drive-thru customers.

'Em, excuse me? We're on bikes,' we replied hopefully.

'No sir, you must be in a vehicle.'

We started making engine noises.

'Vroom, Vroom.'

But that didn't seem to work either. In honesty we were a bit bemused. Why wouldn't they make an exception; we were willing to pay for the food privileges. However things were a bit different over here than in Ireland so we settled instead for a few packets of ready salted crisps in Pufferbellies.

I had arranged to meet Jessica in the club that night. I was to learn a valuable lesson during the course of the evening that, in a funny way, helped me to get the most out of my summer. When she arrived with the rest of the girls, we were sitting in one of the booths. Surprisingly, she avoided me for most of the night. I was baffled. I had really been looking forward to seeing her and the more the night went on the more upset and confused I got. With about an hour to go I decided to leave. As I was going, I bumped into her. She asked me why I was leaving so early and I told her my reasons. I said I couldn't understand what she was playing at and why she was avoiding me. We went over to a corner to get some privacy. She told me she had broken up with someone before she came away and wasn't ready for anything serious at the moment.

I was in a different boat. My ex-girlfriend and I had broken up just short of a year. In that time I hadn't had another girlfriend and in many ways was desperate for a relationship. She had been the love of my life. We were together for two and a half years and when we broke up I was devastated. I went through months of deep depression that I thought would never end. In that deceptively long space of time, I found out what it was like to lose someone special to you and the excruciating pain that accompanies it. Your whole world seems to just collapse, nothing has any meaning anymore, and for the most part you live on a different wavelength and, indeed, a different planet to everyone else.

Without the support of my family and one friend in particular, Fats Tony, who would drag me out onto the golf course every afternoon and try his best to cheer me up and keep me laughing by using his one-of-a-kind personality, I could well have been pushing up daisies as we speak. I had started to feel happier and more positive before I came away. It was slowly starting to get better and I knew coming to America would help me to get back to my old self. I was determined and had the goal in mind of finding someone permanent that I could have a proper relationship with when I got to the States. This, I realised, was the wrong target to aim for and, fortunately, I learned it early on.

Coming to America for the summer should be about enjoying yourself and just being free. A wise man once said that if you go looking for love it will inevitably elude you. Love comes at the most unexpected times and places, you just have to be patient and wait for it. From then on fun times and good craic with friends would be the order of the day and if someone special happened to cross my path then so be it. But as for getting worked up over searching for that perfect person; that philosophy was now abandoned. We both decided there would be nothing serious between us and made a compromise. Despite it not being in either of our natures, we both agreed on a casual relationship. There would be no ties, no rules, we'd be together when the fancy took us and we could be with other people if we wanted – no strings attached.

The next day we were to receive some great news. Jack had, unknown to Michael and myself, gone to Cape Cod Staffing and put his name down for any work opportunities that happened to emerge. He arrived into our room to tell us that the staffing company were looking for three people to put up American banners and flags on buildings on Main Street. There were parades every week during the summer, as well as the July 4th weekend, which in the States is a big event, and many of the shop owners wanted to show their patriotism by displaying their nations colours in the form of bunting on their walls.

There was about two days' work involved in this assignment, and, we were to be paid $11 an hour, which we thought was extremely generous. Caroline, the woman working there, told us to be at the company the next morning at ten. That was perfect, especially since our motel was only across the road, no more than fifteen seconds walk; that's if we weren't mowed down by a Dodge 4x4 on the way over. After all our bad luck, surely faith couldn't have anymore nasty surprises left in store. We kept our fingers crossed.

Slowly but surely, through sheer persistence, people were being rewarded with jobs. The two crazy blonde bombshells from Dublin we first met in the Best Value Inn had got jobs painting. They had to paint huge mansion-type houses that belonged to the rich and powerful. Starting at $8 an hour, Sophie and Isabelle were told this was just to start with and the better they got the higher their wages would climb. Their boss was a nineteen-year old and they were both older than he was. This proved to be a good thing because out of naivety he would leave them to it every morning while he attended to more pressing matters. He gave them a list of things to do for the day and once they finished they could leave.

Little did he know that most days the girls were finished by lunchtime, and still got paid for the whole day. The only trouble they had was with the ladder. It was too heavy for them and they kept telling their boss of their need for a guy to help them with it. Another setback for the girls was their travel arrangements – the boss couldn't collect them, which left them facing the daunting task of cycling forty minutes to and from work everyday. Despite keeping in great shape they were nevertheless jaded performing these daily treks.

The guy they travelled over with, Vincent, who was as sound as they come, managed to get a job working at the docks. It involved long hours and getting up at an ungodly hour. He spent most of the summer working and going to bed early. His reason for coming over was mainly to make money, which was fair enough; everyone had their own personal motives and goals for the summer months.

Patrick, their friend from Cork, found a job in the Hyannis Marina. A hard worker when he had to be, Patrick balanced this out with his aim to enjoy himself, and he would never miss a party or night out. At work he performed almost every duty imaginable from cleaning boats and painting to driving dump trucks and laying tarmac. His boss, however, was a bit of a wanker who made him do every shitty job you could imagine. He helped put an extension on his boss's house because the boss was too scabby to employ professional labourers when he knew he could exploit cheap Irish labour.

Patrick was also handed the charming task of fixing and repairing a huge barge that was responsible for dredging the harbour during the winter. He spent the best part of a month below deck sweating his nuts off because it was made of steel and radiated the sun's warmth.

One of Patrick's friends, who had arrived over a couple of weeks later, got a job within half an hour of getting here. Patrick and himself were walking down the road when a van pulled up beside them and the guy driving asked him if he was Irish. On discovering he was, the driver instantly asked if he wanted to work as a labourer. The Irish are very much sought after for this type of work in America – we are seen as hardworking and loyal (loyal, maybe, but hardworking, questionable). Most of the labouring and landscaping companies had a high percentage of Irish workers on their books.

Only one of the Cork boys from our gang had managed to secure employment. John got a position working in Bike Zone, the place we bought our bikes at the start of the month. This was his third year over on the Cape, and had worked in the bike shop the two previous years. It was a nine to five job, five days a week, so he was guaranteed not to have to work any 'funny' times like a lot of other folk. John was a steady, reliable guy who would do anything for you. He often cured our bike problems picked up along the way, and he didn't look for so much as a nickel in return, although, a bagel was always appreciated by the Doc. He wasn't blessed with height but as everyone agreed, especially the girls, he was very handsome in a charming, subtle sort of way and had a body to die for – can't be a bad complaint to have.

The rest of the boys were, like Michael and myself, jobless. Al however didn't conform to this way of thinking. He used to tell everyone when they asked, that he worked at the beach everyday from twelve till three in the afternoon. People would then ask him if he was a lifeguard and he would stare blankly at them.

'No boy, I work on my tan.'

Jessica and Clodagh were hired by a restaurant on Main Street called Gringo's. As you can guess by the name it was Mexican. It was one of the more popular restaurants in town providing seating inside and out and also on the roof, a romantic setting for that special meal with that all-important person in your life. The majority of the staff was female with only one male waiter charging the floor. The owner was somewhat of a schizo. One minute he would be in a grand mood, the next, he would be shouting the odds and humiliating his staff.

One day during the second week I went there alone to eat as Michael and Emma were spending some time together. I was the only person in the place. People refused to venture out in the lashing rain. An American girl was waiting on me that evening. When I was finished, she brought me the bill and told me she had left her number inside, and if I ever wanted to go out that I should give her a call. I thought I'd pass on the offer cause, putting it mildly, she had a massive arse.

Later on in the summer I found out that she had been sacked for gross incompetence, trying to trick people into ordering the more expensive selection of drinks, and changing tips on people's credit card slips. The majority of the staff loathed her and she had an incurable habit for moaning to the management about fellow employees: was I glad I didn't go out with her ass.

Alyssa managed to swing a job in Fileens, a large and successful department store throughout the US. It was a temporary job and involved carrying out rigorous stocktaking. The hours weren't too friendly; she had to start very early in the morning and usually finished late in the evening, which didn't do much to complement the already intense monotony she had to put up with everyday.

Jeanie and Matilda, the girls from the Cascade, were also on the payroll. Matilda was the newest employee of Schooners, a posh restaurant on Main Street. She got the position of hostess, which suited her. She was a really pretty girl and looked amazing standing outside dressed like a fairy princess trying to entice people in with her elegant beauty. If I had money even for bread I would have taken a seat and nibbled slower than a hamster till the crumbs had disappeared. The job wasn't exactly a dream come through, though. She was being paid $8 an hour, which was fairly poor in relation to the standard of restaurant she was working for. Most of the time she was exhausted from hours of standing on her feet while wearing high heels outside the door, answering people's questions about different dishes and stating the soup of the day every few minutes.

Although the job had its drawbacks, I'm sure Jeanie would have swapped it in a split second for her job. She was working in the Chinese restaurant at the end of Main Street. She was the only non-Chinese employee and couldn't understand a word they were saying. It was a lonely and, to a certain extent, intimidating job. She had to work long hours and at the end of the day she felt like collapsing. Sometimes she wouldn't even get a proper lunch break and would be forced to eat her chicken fried rice intermittently as she ran from tables to the kitchen with orders then back again with the food. The management were very strict and had rules and controls for everything. Her pay wasn't the best either, and she was unsure if she could stick the Chinese 'torture' much longer.

Three of the Cork guys we spent time with, and who also moved east down the road to the Travel Inn from the Best Value Inn, were having their fair share of difficulty finding jobs. They had literally tried everywhere, but to no avail. They were giving themselves another three days to find work otherwise they were going to fly to New Jersey. One of them had a relative living there who could set them up with jobs and a place to stay. They didn't want to leave but their cash was dwindling by the hour, and they faced the very real threat of having to live under the sea. In the end they were forced to leave Cape Cod and moved on to New Jersey where they stayed for the rest of the summer (apart from a brief, two-week holiday two of them took when they returned to Hyannis at the end of August).

Yet, despite the feeling that there were plenty of jobs around, most of us couldn't find one for the love of our mammies. The luck of the Irish hadn't fallen onto us yet. There were a growing number of people starting to ring home to have money sent over. Our house was no different. Some of the lads were down to their last few coins. I was determined not to ring home to ask for help. Before I left Ireland both my Mam and Dad made me promise that I wouldn't hesitate to ask for help if the worst came to the worst.

But I had no intention of doing this. As I said earlier, this was the first time I had lived away from home. I thought that if I could succeed in getting by on my own, it would prove that I had some sort of survival skills and would help make a man of me, while giving me some valuable experience for when I really did leave home for good. In my whole life I never had to work to get by. I never had any real worries or troubles. I always had the support of my family. But now it was up to me. I was looking forward to the challenge even if it meant surviving on a diet of rancid beer and turning into a matchstick man.

If only.

The Dublin gang from the Best Value Inn (I hate calling the motel by this name, it should be called the Cape Cod Detention Centre or the Fierce Expensive Shitty Value Inn) had found a house on the outskirts of town. It was located in a small cul-de-sac, hidden from the world down some narrow country roads. They were throwing a belated house warming party one night, to which we were invited.

Michael and I were the only two of the group to accept the invitation. Patrick said he would meet us at McDonalds (the centre of our universe) to show us the way to the hallowed house because we wouldn't have been able to find it unaided. It was a treacherous cycle as we careered down potholed roads without any sort of light, be it street or bike. I was sure Michael was going to end up in hospital in need of head surgery after driving into a deep crater-like hole. Thankfully, within ten minutes we had made it safely to the party house.

It was an unusual shape. It was long and led down to a lake. There was a deck out the back which overlooked the water. Vincent and Patrick had somehow managed to smuggle a rowing boat back to their own personal dock. It was a good size house. It had to be, there were twenty-one people living there. The house was jammed with people, both Irish and American.

It was a great party while it lasted. The police arrived at about 2am, no doubt called out by some antagonized neighbour allergic to the sounds of laughter – albeit drunken laughter. To my amazement, six or seven squad cars were waiting outside with their head lights directed towards the 'temple of sin'. Once the police show up at the scene you can kiss goodbye to any thoughts of rescuing the festivities. You would have more chance of knocking George Bush off his royal throne in The White House than you would have salvaging the party.

We met Renee, a girl from Dublin, that night. She was here with a load of friends living on Pleasant Street, a sort of mini-complex occupied by fifty or so Irish students. It was across the road from . . . well I won't say the name of the motel, but you get the drift. Out on the road, we were chatting under the parental gaze of the law when a couple of Americans came up and offered Renee a lift home to Pleasant Street.

By this stage of the summer I distrusted American guys immensely and with good reason. I suggested to her that a lift on Martha was available free of charge. She must have felt the same way about the two Americans as she chose the bike over the car. As we were about to jump onto the girls, one of the police officers said he hoped we weren't going to cycle home, as we had been drinking fairly heavily for the best part of the night. As far as I know this constituted drink driving, and was prohibited by law. We told them we wouldn't dream of doing such an irresponsible thing.

A minute later and we were on the road. With Renee on the back and gallons of alcohol cruising through my circulatory system, it was a tough cycle. We couldn't remember the way home, the roads were numerous and narrow and the sky was coal-black without even the moon's light to guide us. As it happened we took a wrong turn somewhere and ended up coming to a dual carriageway. Zonked and totally confused, Renee decided to flag down a biker. I think he must have thought we were stark raving mad. It was about two in the morning and three daft drunks were pulling him over to ask for directions back to town.

Instead of merely giving us directions he offered to show us the way home. He would slowly lead so we could follow him. He offered to carry Renee on the back and she was only too happy to give her ass the pampering it deserved on a leather seat, instead of Martha's hard, skinny saddle. On the cycle back we seemed to go a strange route – it didn't look familiar at all. It was taking far too long to get home and I was a little puzzled by this. After about half an hour we finally came to a place that I knew. It was up beside the golf course, which meant it was still another ten-minute journey to our motel. I was suspicious. It should have taken no more than seven or eight minutes in the first place. How was it taking so long, I wondered.

We finally arrived at Pleasant Street, and we had all sobered up during the prolonged bout of exercise. We thanked the mysterious biker and he left. Afterwards Renee told us why it had taken so long. Our biker friend had an ulterior motive for carrying out this seemingly good and kind deed. He used it as the perfect opportunity to take advantage of a girl and groped Renee all the way home. No wonder it took us an age to get back, the pervert was getting his thrills on the bike. After avoiding the first potential danger with the earlier two guys we were helpless to stop this one.

The next morning was the start of our new job in Cape Cod Staffing. On this occasion we arrived on time – probably because it was only a stone's throw from us. That morning we discovered that the breakfasts were free everyday in the motel. We couldn't believe it, we weren't used to this much luxury in America. Someone must have been playing a cruel trick on us, we thought, and was planning on jumping out and handing us the arm's length bill we had just run up. There was even free tea and coffee all day.

Walking into the staffing office we were introduced to Pat, the owner. He wasn't what you'd call your typical businessman. Wearing a pair of surfer shorts and a T-shirt, he looked like a tourist on a day trip to the Cliffs Of Moher, rather than someone who owned his own company. For the first few banners he would come around and show us what had to be done. Then we set off to decorate the town. He told us some shops had their own banners and flags so we would have to ask for them and inquire as to where the shop owners wanted them to be hung. Pat was a sound guy, full of droll humour, and had the decency to treat us with a bit of respect, unlike our other, brief, employers. Once he had demonstrated the art of hanging, we were now ready to paint the street red, white and blue.

We had discovered the perfect job. We were out in the sunshine and no boss hollering orders at us every couple of minutes – Pat had gone back to the office and left us to it. I cannot tell you how it feels to be earning $11 an hour while chatting to the different Irish people that walked by, counting the number of freaks that passed (so far we were approaching 50%), getting a colour, and literally having the time of our lives.

That day we worked for about eight or nine hours, that's if you could call it work because it certainly didn't feel like it. We got to meet some real characters including this guy who owned a dog memorabilia shop and was as mad as a hatter, insisting he would much rather fuck some hot girls than drink for the night like us Irish do. He was cool. We also had the honour of meeting an African who owned a shop that sold authentic artefacts from his homeland. Even though I didn't quite understand the relevance of owning such a shop in Cape Cod, he was never the less a nice guy. It was undoubtedly the best day's work I had ever experienced and we still had one more day to go. We only wished that this job could last the whole summer.

The next day was just as much fun. It was another day of uninterrupted sunshine. We had some difficulties however. Many of the buildings were made entirely of stone and had absolutely no wooden structures at all. This made it nearly impossible to hang the bunting. On a couple of occasions the ladder was too small to reach up to the place the shopkeeper had picked to put the bunting. We remedied this by going around the back of the buildings, climbing the steel steps and jumping up onto the roof. Though we nearly killed ourselves the odd few times, we did manage to get the flags put up on the shop fronts. All in all it had been a great success and we were expecting the film scripts – that told the story of how three Irish ladder lads overcame all the obstacles and decorated a small American town – to be delivered to our room any time now.

Over the two days we made about $120 each after tax, which to us was as valuable as the Crown Jewels. It meant survival – for another few days anyway. At one point I was down to my last $5, and a packet of honey peanuts that were waiting to be gobbled in my bag. Pat answered an important question we had regarding our difficulty finding jobs and houses. He told us that the reputation of the Irish had suffered over the years. We were regularly missing work from being sick after nights on the tear, we were continuously late for work from being hung over, we managed to destroy the houses we lived in with the parties we threw and, well you get the general gist. Basically we couldn't find jobs or a place to live because of the actions of the previous generation of Irish students. Fair enough, we would probably have the same effect on the next generation.

June was gracefully coming to an end. The weather had drastically improved towards the latter part of the month. Now the days, for the most part, were filled with sunshine and fluffy white clouds that danced merrily in the blue sky, and the rain had ceased to terrorise us any longer. It didn't help either when every report we got from our families back home told of days with heavenly rays of sunlight covering the country. The beaches were filling up and tourists were starting to pollute the area. With the July 4th weekend no more than ten days away, Hyannis was starting to take on a personality of its own.

While the sun was putting smiles on people's faces and lifting moods in every corner its beams touched, there were some, including myself, who faced major financial problems. With the $400 dollar limit on my credit card used up by paying for accommodation, a mobile phone and essential food stocks, and my cash and traveller's cheques all but extinct, my thoughts were solely on survival and not how many hours of sunshine we were getting each day.

The money I had worked so easily to acquire by putting up bunting on Main Street had disappeared without a trace. I had bought a mobile phone for $89, mainly to keep in touch with job opportunities. Michael and Emma had bought two phones over the Internet before they left. These had been delivered out to them a couple of weeks into June, but not without a fair share of difficulty locating them.

Jessica and Clodagh's landlady had given them a brand new phone, not to mention two bikes and blankets (lucky bitches) when they arrived. Every time Jessica wanted to see me she had to text Michael, and, if we weren't together he would have had no way of passing on the message. It just made things that little bit easier by having a mobile each. I had planned originally not to have one at all. In fact, I was looking forward to being free from the curse of the mobile phone. But the way things were panning out at present, I felt I needed one. In saying that most of the people over there got along just fine without phones and I think if I went back again, I'd do without.

One afternoon, as Michael and I tore shreds from our meatball subs, lady luck was to cross my path once again. We ate in this shop-cum-deli most lunch times – they had the tastiest food in Hyannis. The deli was at the back of the shop and was owned by two Brazilians. They were brother and sister and worked more hours than a public telephone. Seven days a week they slaved away in the deli from eight in the morning until ten at night. Except on Sundays when grease junkies couldn't feast on fifty grams of fat after eight. They took no days off, seemed to have no social life and, to make things worse, they lived twenty miles away.

They were talking to us about needing an extra pair of hands behind the counter. I quickly looked down to see if I still had two hands. I did, phew, I hadn't lost them in some drunken rampage – must have been a nightmare. So I offered my services – they seemed glad at my proposal. The brother asked for my number and said he would call me tomorrow. Michael had a little more money than I had and said I could take the job, so that was fine. Hope had waltzed her way back to me.

Life was going well back in the Travel Inn. We were making great use of the facilities on offer. This was luxury which I don't think any of us were expecting. The outdoor pool was proving to be a welcome respite from the heat of the day and during the evenings the hot-pool was a haven of relaxation.

The five of us were developing a new friendship with Fred, the manager of the Travel Inn. To say the least he was a tad unusual, not like your typical hotel manager. Despite his personality slant he was very good at his job and wasn't afraid to use his common sense and calm wit to deal with any problems that arose. He was like our adopted dad, taking an interest in our affairs and looking out for us, always willing to offer advice. The staff consisted of mostly foreigners, the majority being Irish. A girl from Limerick worked behind the reception desk. Julie lived on Pleasant Street along with the masses. There were two more guys that completed the Irish line up. These three formed Fred's elite management team.

As we lived life with a certain cockiness and brashness, we were beginning to take the good times we were experiencing for granted. After all the trouble we had at the start we were making the most of our happy lives and enjoying it.

The Gods decided one day, towards the end of June, to give us a shock, something to remind us that we weren't untouchable. Coming back from a trip to the mall one afternoon Michael had a lucky escape. Wear and tear on the bikes was becoming more pronounced and they had contracted few ailments – dodgy breaks being one of them. Racing down on the path, Michael was leading the way. Out of nowhere a car pulled out of a driveway without so much as a glance in our direction. With brakes that worked about as well as George Bush armed with a pretzel, he swerved out onto the road to avoid smashing into the side of the car. The car continued to pull out without noticing the speeding, worried Michael darting towards him. I shouted at the top of my lungs for the guy in the car to stop. He stood on the brakes missing Michael by the skin of his . . .

That night we got the Doc to fix our brakes.

The following day I kept my phone close by me at all times. I was expecting a call from the overworked Brazilians about the job in the deli. The American girls who were kind enough to help Michael in his minute of need, when he fell off his bike that day at the beach, invited us up to their house for a few jars. They picked us up in their car, so on the way I decided to drop into the deli and find out about the job; persistence was a key virtue in America. I was in for a treat. Almost as soon as I had walked through the door they offered me the position and not just that, they slipped me a free tray of chicken curry, which, must have been a planned temptation to get me to accept the job. It worked.

The girls brought us to Mocha's house. He was the boyfriend of Alice, one the girls, and was renting the place from his neighbour. It was small but homely, and contained all the rudiments; living room, kitchen and bedroom – it was similar to a granny flat. The best thing about the house was its location. It was situated just off the ninth fairway on Hyannisport Golf Club, the course I was interested in caddying on. This allowed Mocha, who was a keen golfer like myself, to sneak on to the course in the evenings when it was quiet to play a few holes. He would bring his dog, Nevada, along for the company.

We listened to some music. Mocha was a DJ on the local radio station and, to our surprise, also organised and ran the Irish night in Pufferbellies every Sunday. He had a soft spot for the Irish and got on well with them, and he was proud of his Irish roots that went back generations. We drank vodka and Red Bull then played some half drunken golf, which is always fun to participate in. After a very enjoyable start to the evening, it was now time to hit Pufferbellies once again.

That night was to make up for the sham of a time I had the previous weekend. Everyone arrived early as people began drinking in the late afternoon and had reached the point where they wouldn't need to drink for the next three hours. The mood was good and everybody, it seemed, was on a high.

We decided to start a volleyball match out the back, on the man-made beach. Despite being dressed up to the nines, with the amount of jar we had our sophistication wouldn't halt us from getting down and dirty. There were about eight or nine people on each team and for two hours, non-stop, we fell around the place in a catastrophic attempt to play the game. The craic was mighty and it was a great way for people to interact. I think we must have played four or five different types of volleyball that night.

The transition to rugby-volleyball turned the game warlike. Nevaeh suddenly got the urge to rugby tackle me to the ground and stuff my mouth with sand (that qualified as my dinner). When the opportunity arose I took sweet revenge and even managed to take one of her shoes. She upped and chased me around the court. I ducked under the net with great agility but Nevaeh ran straight into the rigidly set volleyball net, close-lining her. Her head stayed put while her legs stretched out straight, resembling a wrestler, as she hovered perfectly horizontal in mid-air. She fell flat onto the bumpy, soft sand. The Irish and the Americans saw the hilarity of this and the place erupted into convulsions of laughter and, in fairness to her, Nevaeh laughed as hard as anyone. Keeled over on the ground beside her I had to give back her shoe – she deserved it.

One thing was for sure, that night Nevaeh was the best-known person in Pufferbellies. Again this club had proved its potential and provided us with a night to remember. It was easy to see why it was the best club in Hyannis and, possibly, on the Cape.

The next morning I was up early for my first day working for two zany Brazilians in a deli. They told me that I would be working from eight in the morning until four in the afternoon, Monday to Friday. I was a bit concerned with these hours because our two nights out for the week were Sunday and Wednesday. That meant I would have to get up at seven in the morning, no doubt hung over with a dozy head on me from the night before, and go to work for eight hours.

Bugger.

I learned from the start they were both workaholics, and, just to add a bit of extra spice to things, they were also perfectionists. This attitude didn't fit in well with my way of thinking. First of all I hated working. Secondly the only thing I was a perfectionist about was trying to make it to 'z' before the ring on the beer can snapped off. Despite this I had to swallow my pride. If I didn't malnutrition would surely kill me as seawater and sand were beginning to take their toll.

I discovered the lengths people would go to survive, including myself. We took shitty jobs we would never dream of taking at home – there was no room for preferences. This was the harsh, merciless world we were living in. There was no more protection from your family. You couldn't just go and ask your Da for some money. You now had to pay for everything – food, rent, clothes, drink; sorry, put drink at the top of that list.

Principles and values change when you're desperate, make no mistake about that.

We also discovered a new hobby, stealing. There was no guilt or remorse when you stole to help you get by, it was something you just had to do. Survival of the fittest if you will. Most of the things we nicked were food-based items and things such as cutlery. The fast food chains, KFC and Burger King and the others, provided us with condiments like ketchup, salt, vinegar, pepper and so on. These restaurants also have their drink stations situated out on the floor and not behind the counter as they do in Europe. The reason for this is because when you buy a large drink, refills are free. With most Americans being either overweight or obese, large drinks are normally ordered and it's less of a burden on the staff if people (mammoth mammals) get their own refills. I made particular use of this loophole by asking for a cup for water then filling it up with coke, so at least you got your drink(s) free.

Every little thing you could think of to ease the drain from your pockets helped enormously. Until you are stuck in such a position you would never know the extent to which you could go to keep your head above water. Trivial events such as who came out on top between Man United and Liverpool lost all meaning, and the only thing that mattered was where your next meal was coming from.

The work was tough enough. During the lunch rush the two Brazilians had me running around like a headless chicken. I would dash into the back to fetch ingredients that were needed then leg it back and give them to the lads who would then use them for cooking. The deli was immensely popular with people of all ages in the area. The quality and portion sizes you got were second to none and the food was delicious.

When I wasn't doing this I would be washing pans and carving different types of meat to put them into sandwiches. The deli made its own sandwiches for the shop. They would be put into the fridge and people could just buy them ready-made. It was monotonous, though, making the sandwiches. The Brazilians had a strict structure and way of constructing them. An exact amount of meat and even a certain amount of sauce was pre-decided for each sandwich. If I didn't prepare them in the exact way, I would get a bollocking every time he came to check on my progress, which happened to be most of the time.

I had worked there for two days before I had to take my first day off with a hangover. As I lay on the bed wanting to die, my phone rang. I asked Michael to answer it because I didn't want to talk to the Brazilians. The brother was wondering where the fuck I was as I should have been in work an hour ago. Michael told him, in his best white lie voice, that I was violently ill with a stomach bug most likely attained from food poisoning. This didn't go down well. I could hear the rage in the Brazilian's voice rattle down the line. I decided to pack in the job as I had attended two caddy-training sessions in the last few days. I had previously given up all hope of being a caddy when they told me it didn't start until the July 4th weekend. I thought by then I would have had a job, but since that never transpired I figured what the hell, I'd give it a try.

I went in later that evening and explained to the Brazilians about my up-all-night vomit fest and how it had been the reason for my absence from work. Somehow I don't think they believed a word of it. I then told them about my aspirations to be a caddy, and how it started on Monday morning, so I'd have to leave. I offered to work until then as I was grateful for the opportunity they had given me, even if I was only being paid $6 an hour for my gruelling hardship. They refused my offer and paid me instead. I was relieved. I didn't want to have to cut meat into specifically assigned levels of thickness anymore. The money I had earned should help to keep me going until the caddy season started.

The majority of us were living on very little food. The breakfasts served in the Travel Inn were a blessing in disguise and were our main source of sustenance for the day. We filled ourselves on bagels with cream cheese, which were as popular as tea and toast back home. Cereal, orange juice, coffee, toast and donuts, too, were scoffed down to help us get through the day. Most of the time we swiped a few bagels for a late lunch and this helped to cut our food costs.

Michael and I had discovered the joys of the McDonalds $3.99 salads. This was about all we spent everyday thanks to the Travel Inn's generosity (that had so conveniently eluded the Best Value Inn). Never did either of us think we would see the day when this restaurant would help keep us properly fed with a salad. It was nearly impossible to eat healthy food over there, as it was so much more expensive than its junk counterparts. So I would like to express my gratitude to the biggest fast food chain in the world for its timely invention of the nutritious grilled chicken salad.

6

Arnie?

July had arrived at last. I am happy to report we now had a place worthy of a few choruses of praise to stay, in the Travel Inn, and I had finally managed to find a job, which I prayed, would become permanent. I had heard from many sources that caddying in America was a highly profitable occupation. I was looking forward to starting – maybe then I'd be able to spend more than $4 a day on food. Michael was also able to snag a job at the beginning of July. The Travel Inn was looking for a handyman to work in the motel. His main task would be to paint all the railings and wooden structures around the motel. It was a part-time contract, which would last a couple of weeks and he would work Monday to Fridays. The hotel had agreed to pay him $8 an hour, which was about average. With our fingers crossed and faith strong, we hoped this month would be our lucky month.

Prior to Michael's absorption into the working world, we made the mistake of not paying for our room in time. We were paying by the day and if you hadn't paid by eleven in the morning, the motel took it that you were leaving that day and you lost any reservation you thought you had. For our blunder we were forced to move out of our room and into a one-bed room. This felt like a slap in the face with a slimy fish because it meant we had to pack up all our stuff again. We were furious at both our laziness and ignorance of the situation. But we were getting what we deserved. The room was a sort of little apartment, and under the right conditions could have been seen as an erotic love nest. There were five of us, so we saw it as a cardboard box that was hardly big enough to accommodate all of us.

That night Michael and Emma had a date planned, so they went out for dinner leaving the three of us behind. It turned out being one of the most pleasurable nights I had on the Cape and I'll remember it for a long time to come. It wasn't spectacular in any way and to anybody else it would have been seen as just a run-of-the-mill evening. Jack, Alyssa and I spent the evening watching films on TNT, drinking beer, eating tortilla chips with chocolate cookies and chatting.

These two had been going out for a couple of years and really did make a good team. I didn't know them that well before the summer but they turned out to be two of the nicest people you could hope to meet. There wasn't a trace of snobbery or badness about them, just solid decent folk. Unlike some of the relationships that had travelled to the States, Jack and Alyssa seemed to be thriving on living together in a foreign country, which gave hope to the other struggling couples. The three of us talked about everything from the most trivial of topics such as how good-looking Brad Pitt really was, to the more spiritual and intellectual of subjects. Some people had commented on how they were left out in the cold when they were in the company of Jack and Alyssa but that night nothing could have been further from the truth.

The three of us gelled and I was made feel as at home in their presence as Britney Spears would feel in mine. I suppose when two people love each other to the extent they did it would only be natural that they would want to share every emotion and experience together, giving others the impression of aloofness and a feeling of exclusion. In truth, I think we are all guilty of this and perhaps shouldn't be so quick to judge.

Sometimes those unexpected nights prove to be some of the best and most enjoyable. Once Michael and Emma had come home, drunk as two vagabonds, I was off to Jessica's to stay the night. She and Clodagh had been kind enough to put me up, and it would surely be more comfortable than squeezing into the one bedroom kennel we had in the motel.

In the month I had been there, I had come to a few conclusions about the land of opportunity. Firstly, the 'opportunity' bit seemed to be out of my grasp, if not the grasp of most of the Irish there. It was hard enough to make a buck never mind a few thousand of them. It was damn hard work no matter what job you were lucky enough to get and if you weren't prepared to put in some serious time and effort you would get left behind.

I had severe difficulty in comprehending the reason America was called 'the land of the free'. This, it most definitely is not. There are more rules and regulations than grains of sand on the beaches, most of which were so petty and laughable that it wasn't funny. The feeling of restriction was sometimes claustrophobic; you were nearly afraid to cross the road in fear of getting a 'J walking' ticket. It seemed you couldn't do anything without first making sure it was legal and above board which at the end of the day it probably wasn't. There were laws and rules for everything. There was nothing that wasn't impeccably scrutinised by the authorities to measure its moral standards; and every other standard you could think of.

The more controls you bring in, the more regimented and stifled people become. They become pushovers and happily accept every new freedom-limiting piece of legislation that is made law. The people in America moaned and complained about every little occurrence that passed under their noses. They had no alternative, however, as they had been brainwashed into believing and obeying what they were told. It happened all too often during the summer, like parties that weren't that loud and were causing no one any harm and a thousand other smaller things.

In Ireland we are so much freer than our cousins across the sea despite what they may say. The people of Ireland are much more easy-going and relaxed about things, which, I can only say is the right way to be, a healthier way to live this short life we all possess (although with choking new laws such as the ludicrous smoking ban being introduced, how long this freedom will last is anyone's guess).

There was one thing that baffled me in the States. They obeyed the speed limits down to the very mile, but had no quarrels about having a few jars before driving home. I know we partake in this activity all too often at home but I was surprised to see the stricter more law-abiding citizens of America practising it. We tried to play our part by getting langered then cycling home from the clubs.

So as not to feel alienated, like.

In Hyannis, scraps of evidence were there for all to see concerning laziness. It is a well-known fact that the people in this fair land seem to be losing the battle against the bulge. In America 40% of the population are obese and a massive 60% are overweight, which for the size of the population constitutes a considerable amount of flabby fuckers.

Virtually unknown to us at home, not only restaurants but also chemists and banks employ the drive-thru theory. Imagine not even having to take your large rear end out of your fur-trim seat to run in (or should I say, waddle in) to buy some Rennie to help cure your stomach acid from the five quarter-pounders and ten deserts you had just consumed for brunch.

As for bank robbers they also had it easier. They could just pull up in their tinted-windowed car, hold a gun out, and smoothly voice their demands without having to go through the hardship of running in and out at top speed to get away before the cops arrived. This way, they didn't even have to enlist the services of a getaway driver as they were already at the wheel, saving them precious stolen dollars.

The petrol station system for paying for petrol differed from ours also. You could pay at the pump using a credit card, which to the elation of many a lard-ass cut out that short walk into the shop. Wait a minute, hold the phones – this presented a sticky dilemma. If these people didn't burn a couple of calories by venturing into the shop, how in the world would they be able to buy their cream-filled twinkies. But wait, what's that you say? They could go to Dunkin Donuts, which was also a drive-thru, and purchase three or four chocolate-encrusted donuts with syrup on top. This meant they could do all the errands they required without having to put a foot outside their cars.

They had managed to avoid any situation that required the smallest bit of exercise, and in the process had put on a pound or two.

Victory!

Contact with home was being maintained through a number of different mediums. Most of us would ring home once or twice a week to ease any worries our parents may have had for us and inform them of the goings-on (well, the edited versions anyway). Phone cards could be bought from Apu's and the liquor store. Some had shown their parents how to email before they left and were keeping in touch using this method.

I had neither a home phone nor a computer with internet-capability at home. So I made one call every week to a mobile, which only afforded me fifteen-minutes of talk time compared with two hours on a land line. However, I also wrote a letter home once a week – a fantastic way to communicate and was both personal and descriptive. My family would also send me a hand written synopsis of the news and all the gossip from home. Every Friday I couldn't wait to get back from caddying and open my letter. Not many people used this old-fashioned approach. One person who did was Emma. She often wrote and received a few notes in the post which also succeeded in putting a smile on her face for the day.

The relationships that had formed from the start were still blooming. Bono and Maria were like love birds that were meant for each other. Whenever Maria worked the evening shift as a hostess, she would stare encouragingly across at the clock on the building on the other side of the road as she sat on the little chair at the entrance to the restaurant. The last half an hour or so of her shift was a particularly unfruitful time. She spent that thirty minutes in a trance, fantasising about Bono who would soon be there to pick her up. There was and is nothing more thrilling and emotionally stimulating than being with a person you adore and click with. Maria could have been fired from her job that instant and I don't think she would have batted an eyelid in remorse. There really was quite a powerful connection between the two.

Even disability couldn't come between them. After saying goodnight to his beloved, Bono went home to the motel to share a few drinks with some of the lads. Wide-awake and full of energy, they decided to go for a cycle and watch the sun come up. Somehow, as they were en route to J.F.K beach, Bono got his foot caught in the spokes and nearly sliced his toe off. The large amount of alcohol he had in his system helped deaden the pain but he still had to pay a visit to the Cape Cod Infirmary. His diagnosis was confirmed: a sprained toe along with a monstrous gash. He would have to spend a couple of weeks in a cast with a rather large slipper covering it.

Jacob and Shauna were also becoming closer. They seemed so wrapped up in each other it was like fate had struck. These two had been pierced so many times by Cupid's arrows that they seemed almost indestructible and inseparable. They acted as each other's heart and soul and didn't seem to function as well when they were apart. They had a unique bond and almost seemed detached from the world. Nothing that was said or done could rupture the impenetrable bubble that surrounded them.

These two couples threw a lifeline to every faithless critic that walked the streets of Hyannis and proved that even in today's age, that illusive love most of us spend our lives looking for could be found.

The Travel Inn was the best thing to happen to us since we got to Hyannis. The five of us had a talk and decided to ask Fred if it would be possible to live there for the summer. We had built up a good relationship with the staff and management and I'm proud to say we kept our drunken behaviour to a minimum in the motel. Why ruin a great thing by getting ourselves thrown out because of a drink-induced rave in the room.

Fred told us to ask Andrew, the owner, who was somehow part Irish, as he was responsible for such a decision and assured us he would put in a good word for our cause. This he duly did. Andrew agreed to let us stay as long as we respected the place – in other words once we kept our wild Irish habits at bay. We would be the first Irish group allowed to do this, so our actions would inevitably count either in favour of future occupants of this fine motel, or against them. This place was so much more advanced to the Best Value Inn and the Econo Lodge. And we looked forward to it being our new home for the summer.

Hyannis had, over the last few years, become increasingly dangerous. Cases of violence had risen despite the omnipresent police presence around the area. They patrolled the town on bikes (both motor and push), squad cars and on foot. For such a small town they were everywhere, like ants with fire power running around keeping an eye on things and looking out for any suspicious behaviour. I don't know if it was necessary for the law to keep such a tight rein on the place and on the people, but it did feel as if big brother was constantly watching you, just waiting for you to slip up.

Unfortunately there were times when you needed the police and they weren't there. One night an Irish guy was walking down Main Street. It was after the club, as far as I know. He was wearing a T-shirt, which he more than likely bought when he came over. It sported an NYPD logo on the front. Three black hommies saw what he was wearing and followed behind him. They accused him of being a cop and he tried to set the record straight, but to no avail. They proceeded to beat the living daylights out of him just because he wore this particular T-shirt. After the hiding he ended up in the local hospital and received treatment for his extensive injuries. Despite this attack, occurrences such as this one involving the Irish community in Hyannis were quite rare.

Caution was also needed to a certain extent. One night outside a club, two people were stabbed. They later recruited the services of their gang, hunted down the people who had stabbed them, and shot them in retaliation! This tragedy had occurred for the most farcical of reasons. As one of the guys walked across the floor in the nightclub, the other guy accidentally collided into him, and so it began. Tempers were often fragile and care was sometimes needed to avoid disasters. The mall in Hyannis also played host to an unsavoury situation. The jewellery shop was robbed by a couple of masked gunmen who fired two or three shots, though no one was hurt.

I heard on the grapevine that a carnival had arrived in town, and was set-up in the mall car park. We thought this would be an enjoyable night out so Michael, Jessica and myself decided to go along and see how it compared to Scumbagland – I mean Funderland – my mistake.

When we arrived we met Vincent, Patrick, Isabelle and Sophie. They said it was good but way too expensive; most of the rides were $5 a hit. We could afford exactly one ride. Jessica didn't feel the best so Michael and myself paid our $5 and hopped onto our only bit of excitement for the night. It spun seven different types of shite out of us. We were sick and dazed after the bloody thing – we would have had to drink a bottle of whiskey to feel like that. We strolled around the park trying not to vomit, while gazing at all the different rides, bright lights and fat carnies who tried their best to lure us over and get us to play their pre-determined games.

We stumbled upon a booth where you could pay to see the world's smallest woman and it only cost a dollar. We had to see her, even though we realised it was probably a hoax. More than likely it was a doll that looked like a woman or a cardboard cutout from a Coco Pops box.

We paid over our last few dollars and went to gawk at the little lady behind the counter. She was sitting down which probably made her appear smaller than she really was. Apparently she measured twenty-nine inches in height but her appearance didn't amaze us in any way. There was no 'wow' factor. In fact, when she saw Michael, she started laughing and pointing her finger at him trying her best to encourage us to join in and have a laugh at his expense. I thought Michael was going to pick her up and drop-kick her across the fairground giving her a butter bath in the crate of popcorn just purchased by a widening twelve-year old. It was an entertaining encounter with the little freak on the chair. Our visit to the carnival was short and sweet – the downfall and stark reality of being broke.

A day before I was scheduled to begin my caddy career Jack had been offered a job by the staffing company, and they needed two more people. Every year the Kennedy family threw a huge elegant party at their mansion beside the sea, not far from the golf club. The staffing company needed people to work at this party. It took me about a millisecond to make up my mind. The caddying could wait another day.

The next morning we were awake early for breakfast. The party wasn't starting until four in the afternoon but everything had to be organised and set up. Altogether there were about nine of us contracted to work for the day. There were two Russians but apart from that it was all Irish. We got a lift from Pat in the minivan and within five minutes we stood agog staring at a beautiful white mansion that was owned by the Kennedys. What a place to work for a day, it was magnificent. On top of this most years the one and only Arnie would attend the famous function. It would make our life if we could get to meet him, as he was a personal hero of Michael's and mine – we worshipped the guy.

The first thing we had to do was lay out dozens of wooden tables and chairs. While we were doing this, Michael and I were asked to go out to the beach, which was literally down the garden path, and dig a hole for the bonfire they lit every year. We gladly accepted, as it was an opportunity to relax and catch some rays on the sand. The organisers had given us a big box with ice, filled with fizzy drinks and water to help keep us hydrated throughout the day. We managed to swipe a couple of beers from the house and sneak them down to the beach in a big wheelbarrow under the firewood. We needed refreshment that particular day because the temperature had soared. We took our time digging the hole, and very slowly filled it up with fire logs so we could enjoy our newly stolen beer.

One of the Irish guys who was working there that day was, to say the least, a bit of an oddball. We had briefly met Herbert a couple of weeks back but we really got to know the real Herbert at the Kennedy Compound that afternoon. After a few hours' work, we were all treated to pizza from the Italian down the road. We had worked up quite an appetite since the early morning and devoured it like lions. But not Herbert. Herbert didn't like pizza crust. When he told us this we near shit ourselves laughing. What sort of eejit doesn't eat pizza crust, especially when you're famished from the hunger. We felt like taking the pizza off him altogether and depriving him of his lunch.

During the meal he confessed to us his desire to be a waitress. Was this idiot for real. He had been called by the staffing company the previous week and they told him they had a day's work arranged, and that he had to be there for six in the morning the next day. The next morning he showed up at the company promptly and was looking forward to a nice pleasant day's work. He asked Pat what type of job he would be doing. Pat replied that it was landscaping.

Apparently Herbert's face went a pale white as if he had seen something from the great beyond. He flatly refused the job, declaring that he didn't like that sort of work, letting Pat down in the process. This guy in simple English was a pussy and he didn't deserve pizza. He should have been made eat every crust in the box – that would have given him something to whine about. Despite this, we had great craic ribbing him, and he gave us something extra to laugh about during the summer. God bless you Herbert.

We worked for about fourteen hours in the Kennedy's, but it equalled hanging up bunting on the buildings on Main Street for enjoyment. We worked hard setting everything up before 4pm – organising tables and chairs and decorating the tables with little tasteful ornaments for July 4th.

Once the party started it was smooth sailing from then on in. We spent the rest of the day playing soccer beside the pool with the kids. I don't think many of the adults were too amused with this as a few of them got unexpected blows to the head by the ball. When we got tired kicking the kids around in soccer (and literally), we headed over to the portable Ben And Jerry's stall to chat up the two attractive girls who had been hired for the day. They worked in the Ben And Jerry's shop on Main Street. One of their fathers owned it. We pigged out on chocolate chip and cookie dough ice cream for the afternoon and followed it with numerous cheeseburgers and hot dogs. We started to wish it could be like the film *Ground Hog Day* so we could have the pleasure of reliving that July 4th over and over again.

After the party, we cleaned up everything and put away all the furniture. To our visible disappointment Arnie didn't turn up. Rumour had it he was in Europe promoting *T3*. But we did get to see the Kennedy family, even if they had to be pointed out to us cause we didn't have a clue what they looked like. Other than that the day had been a tremendous success, and the organisers commended us on a job well done. We ate like Kings, had the honour of celebrating July 4th in the Kennedy Compound, and had the satisfaction of teasing Herbert. The Ben And Jerry's girls also invited Michael and myself to their shop for free ice cream whenever we wanted. We earned about $130 each for our laid-back graft, including a generous tip from the Kennedys. Now it was time to go back to the motel and dream that we were with Arnie on his promotional tour.

Spirits visit at night
when there is no light

7

July had started with a bang and so far things were going great. To our delight they were about to get even better. Coming home from the beach one sunny afternoon, Emma passed a house that had a 'For Rent' sign in the garden. Out of pure curiosity she took the number, not even expecting to have any sort of chance – this house was surely out of our reach. She rang the landlady to enquire about the property. Emma was told the potential occupants could move in on the twelfth of July. The landlady told Emma that she lived in Boston, and if she was interested in renting the house she would have to pay the weekly rent through the bank, as she didn't have time to drive out to Hyannis every week to collect the money.

Emma turned on her subtle charm and cunning to exploit this perfect opportunity. As sharp as a pin, she coolly told the landlady in question that there were five of them wanting to stay in the house, and that they were all girls. This was an ingenious move that was to see the nine of us moving into the house for the best part of two months. The landlady had no problem letting the house to five innocent girls who would never think of causing trouble. As she lived two hours away, she would have no idea there were three guys and an extra girl living there as well. After a month of searching every nook and cranny for a half decent place to live, Emma had managed to orchestrate, in the space of a couple of minutes, the perfect house which we could all move to.

They do say the best things come to those who wait. That's not to mention being evicted and run out of motels and facing just about every sort of obstacle that could possibly stand in your way.

That evening we told Fred back in the Travel Inn about our good news. There was now no need for us to stay in the motel, so we thanked this classy guy for all his help, and the fact that he had put in a good word for us with Andrew. We would have a week left in the Travel Inn, and then it would be time to pack up once again and move on, hopefully, to our last place of shelter. Until then we would make the most of our complimentary breakfasts, our evening handball matches in the pool (which the cranky Russian tried to put a stop to, but never could), and divine sessions of relaxation in the hot tub.

My first day of caddying started off very unusually. On my way up to the course I was to be the object of someone's affections. As I booted along the coast road admiring the picturesque scenery, that acutely resembled the backdrop to *Dawson's Creek* (wasn't that a great little show), I noticed in the corner of my eye a person staring over at me. I gazed across to see a man on a bike on the other side of the road. As we passed each other I looked back to see his eyes were still fixed on me. I suddenly had a thought that he knew me from somewhere or maybe I knew him. Being your typical ignorant, gullible Irish guy, I decided to slow down and stop. Within a matter of seconds he had bound across the road and over to my side. As he stood there beside me, topless, I suddenly had a reality blast and realised what a gobshite I was.

'Hi, I've just been in for a swim,' opened the forty-year old beefcake.

'Ah sure, fair play to ya,' I replied in a slightly nervous voice.

'So what have you been up to today then?'

'Nothing much, just out looking for a job.'

'I'll give you a job.'

'Oh ye, doin what?' I foolishly asked.

Looking me up and down, paying particular attention to my young ass, and with a smirk that would make your skin wither, he eagerly replied.

'Anything!' in his most seductive, gay voice.

With that I told him I had to go, I was late, then made a dash for it. I cycled as fast as my legs could turn the pedals of my bike as this guy looked fit and strong. I now know how girls feel when they are continuously hit on by muscle men. I'm not small, and I don't shirk from trouble, but this guy was scary and I did feel extremely intimidated. All I wanted to do was get away from him.

I realised after that episode what a lot of girls have to put up with. Every time I was out after that in clubs and so on, my heart would go out to those girls who were being hounded and harassed by these brainless goons as they tried to enjoy themselves. Many of them fail to get away from these prying predators. I wondered how many girls are forced to give in, even in small ways, to such pressure, in order to escape any further agitation. There is no worse feeling in this world than being in a situation you can't get out of, and you are being overpowered by some evil son of a bitch who has taken away your rights and freewill. And through lack of strength, or choices, has made you succumb to your own primitive fear, allowing him to exploit you.

A week later, dressed in flowery pink shorts, our local gay hit man targeted Bono for his next advance. It took him a while to clasp his sexual intentions, and Bono couldn't wait to get back to the safe bosom of Maria when he eventually figured out what was going on.

Cycling away, my first day at caddying went well. I was hardly there half an hour when I was called to do a double bag. Even though I played golf regularly I had never caddied before, and now I was being entrusted with two bags not just one. Four hours later, and a couple of minor hitches here and there (including losing someone's 3-wood head cover), I had earned my first dollars as a professional (and I use that term loosely) caddy.

They had a system in the golf club whereby the caddies were split into two groups, category A and category B. The A's would get paid a minimum of $20 plus tip, while the B's got $16 and a tip. Myself and the other five or so Irish caddies received the accolade of being placed in the A group. The average wage for us was $30 for a single bag and $60 for a double, which was a pittance when you consider the wealth of the club and its members. To be lucky enough to be accepted into such a fine establishment, you then had to fork out the massive joining fee of $50,000. The generosity of most of the members wasn't exactly what you'd call, 'generous'. You just kept your mouth shut and got on with the job, happy with what you got.

At this time, people were starting to receive their exam results from home. Most people had the good fortune of passing, and with each story of success people brought celebrations ensued. As the old saying goes, 'any excuse for a party', and we certainly honoured this long held tradition. Deco was the only one from our gang to fail. He failed two subjects which would mean an earlier than planned return home. Frustration struck. The summer was going great and everyone was having a ball. Deco felt deflated, as going home prematurely would almost certainly mean the missing out on many irreplaceable, memory-shaping moments. He had a month before he would have to fly home and hit the books. So until that day arrived he would party harder than ever before, and believe me, that was a tough thing to accomplish.

As I waited on my Dad to collect my results from the house, I was just about to pick up the payphone when out of nowhere a woman appeared. She asked me if I was using it and I said I was on the verge of calling home. Surprisingly she retorted that it was a public phone and she was going to use it. Before I had a chance to react she asked.

'Are you Irish?' I nodded.

She stated, determinedly, that she was part Irish and that she, too, had an Irish temper. She was quite fat and I imagined she must have won the annual donut eating competition in Hyannis every year, without fail. I just smiled and told her to drive on and make her call. Anyway, I thought her Irish temper might have tempted her to raise her leg as high as it would go and kick me in the shin. My results could wait.

The first disaster of July happened about a week into the month. Jessica and Clodagh had laundry facilities in a little room at the back of their house so, instead of going to a normal Laundrette, I decided I'd take my clothes to the girls' house to be cleaned.

It was all going swimmingly, until I stepped into the little room where the machines were located. If there had been any justice in the universe, God, or some other mysterious force would have subconsciously stopped me from ever entering that most regrettable of places. On top of the washing machine was a big bottle of bleach. After dumping in most of the clothes I had brought over to the States with me, which wasn't much (I like to travel light so I can build up more speed running along the travellator in the airport), I proceeded to empty the only bottle in sight onto my clothes.

As I pored the liquid onto my unsuspecting, innocent attire, Michael in a not-so-confident tone of voice enquired into the relevancy of my actions. I told him, surely, that it was grand, and wasn't that what the bottle on top of the washing machine was for. Before I had time to even close the lid on the machine, I noticed my clothes were starting to change colour. Becoming slightly anxious, I picked up a few articles and pretty much gasped in horror as I saw that they were becoming multi-coloured.

I had only brought three pairs of trousers with me, and currently two of them looked like the offspring of rampant rainbows. The first were a pair of jeans, which had become a cross between existing blue and several patches of white, with a particular pattern on the crotch. The other pair were dark navy-blue going-out trousers, which now looked like the private evening wear of that middle-aged guy who took time out of his busy schedule to chat me up the other day. Designs of pinkie-red mixed in quite gaily with the traditional dark navy-blue colour that had originally dominated the trousers. T-shirts, socks and underwear, too, did not escape the carnage.

Realisation kicked in soon after that I was poverty-stricken and couldn't afford to replenish my clothing supply. I figured that the substantial gay community in Hyannis might like me more in this sort of get-up. I had been hit on a few times already by the 'oh what a gay day' brigade, including once in the gym, which isn't the kind of thing you want as you sit there sweating from lifting weights. Inevitably, I was the laughing stock of the Irish community.

Even Jessica's mam, who came over for a couple of weeks with her little brother to visit, couldn't contain her judgemental laughter. In my defence, things domestic were never my strong point and home economics wasn't part of my academic make-up. So I plead that my apparent stupidity be put down to this. I've decided that whenever I go away in the future, I'm taking my mother with me so disasters like this will never again occur.

That night I was to have an encounter with the spiritual world. We only had a few days left in the Travel Inn when this bizarre incident took place. It was deep into the night and darkness smothered every corner. The five of us were out for the count and I was asleep in my rightful place on the mattress on the floor. I was rudely awoken by the screaming of my mobile phone that lay next to my head.

When I picked it up, it displayed 'private number' on the screen. This was weird for a couple of reasons. Firstly, I always switch my phone off at night because I like my privacy and don't particularly appreciate being woken up in the middle of the night, unless I'm going out with someone and then I don't mind. Secondly, ever since I bought the phone I never had 'private number' appear on the screen because I had very few numbers registered and not many people had my number.

I answered it and sleepily said.

'Hello?'

No reply. That was strange.

'Hello?'

No reply once again. There didn't seem to be anyone at the other end of the line. A feeling of inevitable dread swept over me. It seemed like too much of a coincidence that the one night I neglected to power off the phone I would experience this unusual occurrence. I quickly pushed the button at the top of the mobile to turn it off. Now I couldn't be troubled or haunted by any roaming spirits that happened to be around the place. I quickly sought shelter in the unconscious world. I'm a very heavy sleeper and knew that once the sandman did his job I would be out till morning.

This didn't happen. Approximately ten minutes later, I couldn't be totally sure, my eyes shot open as if they had just been poked with something sharp. The second my eyelids lifted, a shadow walked across the corner of my bed just inches from my face. I sat up instantly and whispered loudly.

'FUCK OFF!'

I thought it was a person who had broke into the room. This had absolutely no effect. The shadow walked straight over to the entrance of the bathroom and stopped. I thought I must have been imagining things so I closed my eyes and rubbed them for a few seconds. When I glanced over in the direction of the bathroom, the shadow took the form of a man and it stood firmly there.

I was dumbfounded and sat frozen to the spot (just as a nation was when they waited to see if Keane could rectify Harte's blunder against the Spanish). I watched this amazing spirit who seemed to be waving at me – his left hand was moving from side to side. I peered around the room to see if there was any light coming in which may be causing this trick to be played on my eyes. But there wasn't.

I looked over to the other beds and quietly asked if anyone was awake; there was no reply. I figured it would be best to keep my mouth shut after that in case I irritated the figure from the realms of the unknown that was standing at the entrance to my bathroom. After about five minutes of relentlessly staring at the spirit, I contemplated going back to sleep. He didn't seem dangerous or evil in any way, as he hadn't shown any signs of aggression. So I put the sheet over my head and travelled back to the land of nod.

The next morning I was up at six for caddying. This was a severe drawback to the job; mixing me and early mornings was like mixing Baileys and Bulmers – an angry layer appears. The bright, temperate dawns made it that much easier to jump out of bed – without those I think I'd still be asleep dreaming of making my fortune by caddying. When I had the money I would eat some toast for breakfast with peanut butter, to which I had become addicted during my stay in America. The rest of the time I would grab a bar of chocolate or a packet of peanuts in the little shop in Hyannis Port. In America, bread was surprisingly expensive, as if it was a luxury food rather than a necessity.

I learned, to my dissatisfaction, that by leaving the motel shortly after six, I would arrive at the golf club close to half past and the caddyshack would already have a minimum of seven or eight 'little shits' waiting in line to go ball hunting. Since work was based for the most part on a first come first serve basis, sometimes I would be waiting around for two or three hours to get a 'loop', while the kids in front stumbled clueless out onto the course.

The weather was beautiful now and the days were hot and humid. Most of the golfers would neglect to play during the hottest part of the day, which was pretty much after eleven or twelve. So if you didn't manage to get out in the morning, you could throw in the club-logo towel and go home, which happened a fair bit. The club didn't exactly work hand in hand with the caddies to ensure that it was a profitable and worthwhile week for all. The golfers had the option of taking a cart instead of a caddy. For the most part, the staff first asked them if they would like to take a cart, which didn't do much to promote our prospects (the art of walking is a dying notion in America).

It wasn't the most ideal job by any means. A lot of the time you were forced to wait around with no guarantee of work, and, for me, that might mean no breakfast. On one occasion, as we were leaving, there was a lady golfer in the car park who had five or six boxes to carry in from her car. She paid four of us twenty dollars to bring them in for her. We made five dollars each and were ecstatic as it meant we could afford food for the day (Mmmmm, bread).

The sweltering weather played a huge part in the life of the caddy. As you struggled to carry two bags full of clubs around eighteen holes for the guts of four hours – following each player as they sliced another ball into the trees leaving you the responsibility of finding it – near full humidity and a baking sun that blasted your body did you no favours. There were water taps after every three or four holes. Without them I think we all would have collapsed dead from dehydration and left to be picked clean by vultures. After the gruelling round had ended (and with little recognition or thanks for a job well done) all you wanted to do was get on your bike, go home, and relax in front of the TV with an ice-cold beer.

Despite these unsavoury factors, you were your own boss – you could come and go whenever you pleased and work whenever you wanted. It's nice to have that sort of freedom without the suffocating restraints of nasty employers who treat you like something they had just cleaned off their shoe. On top of this, if you managed to get a loop in the morning you would be finished by mid-day. Then you had the rest of the day to relax and do whatever took your fancy, be it the beach or the mall or whatever. From then on I realised I would have to work quite hard to survive, and my time of rising would be appropriately, yet painfully, dragged back half an hour.

Later that day when I came home with my well earned $60, I was asked by Emma how I had slept. I looked at her and broke into a wry smile.

'Funny you should mention that.'

I told her about my spooky encounter, and to my astonishment and sheer joy she had also seen our friendly visitor. She had seen the ghost the previous night just like myself. Emma had woken from her sleep just as unexpectedly and spontaneously as I had. She had a feeling that there was something in the room – she could feel a presence. Crawling to the foot of the bed, she looked left towards the bathroom where she gazed upon the same eerie human-shaped shadow I had seen. A feeling of fear spread through her and she raced back up the bed and under the covers.

This wasn't her only sighting of the spirit. A couple of days beforehand she had woken up and saw something sitting on one of the chairs in the corner of the room. She told Michael, who was still awake next to her, that there was something in the corner. Michael dismissed her assertion, and put it down to Emma's regular sleep talking, which she suffered from, and he fell asleep without another thought on the matter.

I knew what I saw that night in the room, but Emma's confirmation of the ghost's existence (if you can say such a thing) reassured me beyond all doubt of the truth. When I told Jack and Alyssa (in my best story telling voice), Jack thought I was barmy, or perhaps suffering from the effects of a lifetime of drinking. To this day I still don't think he believes me. Alyssa, her eyes opening wide filled with terror, nearly collapsed from fright as I described the goings-on. For the remaining nights we stayed in the Travel Inn, Alyssa would not remain in the room on her own, and wouldn't contemplate going to bed without someone being there. Who knew if the spirit would decide to pay another visit to our part of the building.

We told Fred about these strange happenings and he remarked that there had been previous sightings of the spirit in the past. I have to say I felt the same way as Alyssa to a certain extent. Every time bedtime came along shivers shot through me at the thought of a ghost sequel. To try and make sure it didn't happen again, I took to having a few drinks before I hit the sack, hoping that falling into a deep coma-like slumber would protect me. We escaped any further visitations from the spectre that lived on the cusp of both worlds.

During our stay in the Travel Inn some unscrupulous individual took it upon himself to rob a few of the bikes that were parked against the railings outside the rooms. Thankfully neither Honey nor Martha was taken as we had locked them (though Martha was later abducted in a heartless act of thievery, but fortunately Deco managed to retrieve her). Friends of mine suffered this fate and I really did feel for them because without your bike you felt somewhat isolated and stuck.

Emma's pride and joy was nicked in the raid. She was a little more than peeved when she found out she was bike-less the next morning. The thief should count his lucky charms that he wasn't discovered because I think Emma would have indulged in a little game of castration, without an anaesthetic, and then stuck a whole mountain bike where bikes aren't meant to go. Lacking the relevant discretionary cash, people had to fork out to buy new bikes and were then forced to go without the basic necessities such as food, or even worse, drink.

This wasn't the only time our trusted transportation system was targeted. Back in the Best Value Inn, when the place was sound asleep dreaming of cycling their bikes in the next day's sunshine, the tyres on nearly every bike were ruthlessly slashed. There was a suspicion that the weird guy in the white van may have been the culprit, or maybe even one of the bike stores in a greedy attempt to exploit more money from the impoverished Irish. We never discovered the perpetrator of these crimes but I can safely say, whoever it was, must have had a car.

Back on the job front, the staffing company offered Jack a permanent position landscaping. It was decent if not spectacular pay and probably should have been more. He had to be outside Cape Cod Staffing before 6am every morning. Pat would give himself and a couple of boys from Northern Ireland (whom we had met at the J.F.K party and who were now good friends) a lift to the landscaping company's base. Chris, Bono's friend and partner in crime, was also employed in this line of work. He was a quiet individual; though after a few mouthfuls of Rubinoff a carefree and blithe side was revealed.

The base was located a few minutes down the motorway and car was the only way of getting there – unless you felt brave or stupid enough to go for it on the rothar. The work was tough. Jack and the lads would do anything and everything from digging massive bunker holes to laying out turf and so on. He was working at the opulent homes of the local nobility. In fact a lot of the places he worked were only holiday homes, not people's normal homes. Hundreds of thousands, if not millions, would be spent on their gardens and they would only spend a couple of months a year there.

Carrying out a job like this for people wasn't the same personal experience it was in Ireland, where the workers would kindly and appropriately be brought out a cup of tea and a few Jacobs biscuits every now and then. Unfortunately the more money people have the tighter they become. They could afford to offer a comprehensive array of bickies – on a gold-plated tray – for the worn-out workers; though I suppose colonic irrigation is important, too.

I remember Jack telling me that one family paid $40,000 for a tree that was to be planted in the garden. Not wanting it to flap in the wind on its own they bought two – that's a lot of McDonalds dollar menu meals for a tree. Jack would often come home with a bright red face that had been battered by the sun while it was high in the sky. Normally he would arrive home between six and seven in the evening, fly down the road to Micky Ds, and savage a big dinner after his long laborious day's work.

Alyssa meanwhile was offered a full-time job in Fileens, the large department store in the mall which sold just about everything. A couple of weeks before she was offered the job, she and Jack had invited me out to dinner in Gringo's. At the time Gringo's were looking to hire more staff for the busy season. We managed to persuade Alyssa, through no lack of effort, to apply for a waitressing position by reminding her of her traits and potential for the job. Alyssa was, by nature, a bit shy and retiring and wasn't filled with confidence about her ability for the job. In the end, fair balls to her, she swallowed hard and went for the available position.

Facing her fears and putting herself on the line for personal criticism or failure was a very brave and noble act. Yet, after all of our inspired persuasion and support, the manager wasn't there and she was told to call back the next day. Ultimately she never did call back but she had overcome her nerves that day and Jack and I witnessed the courage she showed.

In Fileens the hours were long and unsociable and she had to work a five-day week. There were a few Irish working with her including Renee's friend, Sarah. The two girls acted as each other's work mates and lunch buddies – it was better to have someone to hang out with, less lonely.

But the most notable Irish employee was... our old friend, Herbert! He had finally gotten the soft cushy job that he was looking for. The restaurants he had applied to must have turned down his desired 'waitressing' position based on equality issues. I think he was responsible for the handbag section in the store, which would have been right up his feminine alley.

Even Alyssa, who was fair and kind, saw the hilarity of this and couldn't but help make a couple of critically funny observations.

Most of the girls that had come over with me were now working full-time in the Duck restaurant. Sheila was hired shortly after arriving and Shauna was stretching herself to the limit by waitressing in the restaurant and working part-time in Fileens. They would have a mixture of waitressing responsibilities and filling the post as the hostess. They were paid a fixed hourly rate of $8 when they acted as the hostess as there were no tips involved, whereas they would be paid the bare minimum as waitresses as most of their wage would be based on tipping.

It's true that a lot of money could be earned working as a waitress but when the weather was bad and the restaurant empty, the girls made sweet fanny adams. This didn't help if you were trying to get the last $30 together to pay the rent and have enough left over to replenish the battery supply to your hair dryer. The girls just had to keep their fingers crossed that the rain would hold off till morning, or hope the inhabitants of Hyannis were starved with the hunger.

Gringo's staff was having more in the way of a lucrative summer. Jessica and Clodagh were regularly coming out with over $100 in tips for a few hours' work. A handful of times this figure passed the $200 mark. Gringo's was a more popular and busier restaurant than its rival down the street and, in fairness, did serve the nicer food. They also had a tequila menu with over twenty-five different kinds to choose from, with one particular brand costing a hefty $60 per shot. Gringo's had less quiet nights than the Duck, so the girls could normally expect to have gorgeous straight, dry hair.

Renee and a few others, including Jessica's friends, were working in a restaurant called the Clam Shack at the end of Main Street. This was a little bit more up-market than the previous two restaurants and in turn employees got paid accordingly. I think the employee profile of every restaurant in the town showed the majority of the workforce were made up of Irish people (the Americans didn't know what hit them when blunt naturalness came into play and sickening superficiality went out the window).

Nevaeh and Clare were now settled in their job. They were working nights in the Christmas Tree Shop out near the mall. This must have spawned from Nevaeh's outrageous subconscious with the aim of finding something different and unusual to work at. It was their job, and the job of the entire non-American workforce for the most part, to load the shelves with products. I reckon the founder must have been high at the time he or she came up with the name for the shop because they sold everything that had nothing to do with Christmas.

Clare, who wasn't much of a night owl, used to sneak off to the toilet for a forty-five minute snooze to catch up on some much-needed kip. She was caught a few times but I don't think it deterred her from her nightly forty winks. Despite working overnight they were only paid $8.75 an hour, which didn't seem to warrant staying up all night. They would work from eleven until half seven in the morning. I met them a couple of times coming home when I was on my way up to the golf course to start my day's work. The lads would then go home and sleep till the late afternoon.

Michael was working away every weekday helping to give the motel a cosmetic face-lift. He was working with a Jamaican lad who did nothing but talk about his desire for sex and his fondness of drugs. Michael would retaliate with constant reference to drink and Fr Ted. If you were to blend these two people together you would no doubt come up with the world's most infamous raving hellcat. Or even the next Taoiseach of Ireland. It wasn't the most charming of work. He spent most of the time covered in dust and paint but it was a handy job that was close to home; or even was his home. It was only on a part-time basis so he would be finished soon.

While Michael was busy improving the motel, his girlfriend got a call from the staffing company across the road asking if she had any interest performing some light, house-keeping duties. It sounded like a nice relaxing stroll in the park, so Maria and Emma agreed to take it on. What a pity people don't have access to hindsight, because when they came home that evening smoke literally oozed out from their ears and their eyes were bloodshot. It had been the most horrible and disgusting job they ever had to do. The owners of the motel applied continuous pressure on them to clean the rooms better and faster. They had to carry out such chores as changing sheets (who knew what substances were scattered across these the previous night) and cleaning toilets. Their noses were filled with the intoxicating odour of bleach and other cleaning products that made them feel as if they had just guzzled a litre of space-tea in Amsterdam. Overall the work was torturous and afterwards they vowed never to house clean again.

That Sunday, before Pufferbellies, Michael and myself went to visit Matilda. Jeanie, her best friend, had abandoned her to go to a concert in Boston. Matilda wasn't able to get the time off work so she had to stay in Hyannis missing out on a wild weekend in the city.

I decided to sport my gay combination, which consisted of a pair of navy trousers with pinkie-red patches along with a similar-looking T-shirt (I also had the same boxers on, too, in case any doubts remained). The three of us spent about an hour getting sauced up on vodka and orange juice before hitting the club. This must have been too long drinking double shots because when we went outside the room, Matilda swayed from side to side like a flag in a light hurricane. We helped her down the stairs of the motel and pretended she was sober by walking arm in arm past the reception desk, hoping to conceal her rather fragile state from the owner who stood gazing inquisitively at us.

In the club, there was a big game of volleyball organised. I spent my time jumping up to slam the ball home for a point then running over to see how Matilda was getting on. In the hours we were there she didn't seem to sober up at all which meant I was stuck with the responsibility of watching out for her, which I didn't mind as she had become a good friend. One of the head bouncers saw her staggering around the place and came over demanding she be evicted from the club. She wasn't wearing a band around her wrist so he knew that she was underage, which incensed him even more. I explained that she had a few drinks at home and not in Pufferbellies and that I was looking after her. After a bit of persuasion, he let her stay on the threat of expulsion if any trouble was caused. In actual fact she was regularly thrown out of Pufferbellies for being drunk without the relevant colourful bracelet to prove her legality.

My altered attire seemed to be getting a mixed reaction from people. The Americans thought it was normal and probably styled purposely to create an effect; while the Irish got a great laugh out of taking the mickey out of my newly bleached clothes and thought the prolonged sun exposure had finally gotten to me (some even stood against the wall as I passed). By the end of the night I tended to agree with them. But without the money to buy some respectable, non-crayola-basted gear, I was stuck with the gay look for a while. I just had to get used to it.

It seemed every time I turned around some skanky maggot was hitting on Matilda. Couldn't they see she could hardly stand. One time she was chatting to an older guy at the bar who looked as sly and untrustworthy as they came. I went over to try and give her a break from his constant leering. It was at the end of the night so I took her outside.

The guy she had been talking to was one of the chefs from the restaurant she worked in. They had been seeing each other for a while. As it turned out, he had dumped her because of her reluctance to sleep with him. She had only known him for a couple of weeks and didn't want to get that involved that quick. He was the kind of guy who deserved to have his dick locked up in some sort of chastity belt and then left in a room full of naked girls.

Then see how it feels.

Matilda made the right choice and I tried my best to explain this to her. She was a lovely person and deserved a million times better than this cretin. It would be his loss and it couldn't happen to a nicer individual.

After the club, I walked (helped) Matilda home to her motel room. When we got there she decided that she was peckish and wanted to go to Christy's to buy a meatball sub. She wanted to cycle there, which in her drunken state could have meant disaster. I had visions of her careering down the one-way road that led to

Christy's, swerving from side to side undeterred by the fact she was engaged in a game of chicken with a ten-ton truck. I told her I would take the bike and get her the sub she craved and I'd be back in five minutes. She slurringly agreed. When I arrived back at her room carrying her mini-feast, she was down for the count on the sofa and probably dreaming of a meatball sub all the way from Christy's. I promptly took my leave and went home to hit the pillow.

One day, as I was on my way to the mall, I ran into Larry and his wife. Mr Miagi again became the focus of the conversation. He had raised the rent so high they weren't able to afford to live there anymore. What had been their home for the past few years had now been swiped away from them in one cruel gesture by greedy, heartless Chinks. We spent the better part of a few minutes bad mouthing the people who had made our lives a misery, and then went our separate ways.

8

Wow!
– Our very own place

Reports from Ireland were telling of hundreds, if not thousands, of Irish students being forced to return home early, due to a severe lack of jobs and accommodation. In one phone call home to my Mam, she told me that this backward migration was being documented regularly and talked about on the Gerry Ryan Show. She said that they were estimating as much as 45% of the travelling Irish to America had made the premature quest home.

I understood their plight. Most of us in Hyannis had gone through the same thing but had managed, somehow, to dig our heels in and hold on. One of the places worst hit was San Diego. Lucky for Michael, Emma and the rest of the gang they rooted for Cape Cod instead. I knew, once I heard what was going on in different parts of America, how blessed I was to have chosen to travel to the Cape, and how mightily dejected I would have been to have had to go home before my time.

It was only a couple of days before we would make the move into our new and, with the grace of the good Lord, permanent residence. Despite the hardship being endured by hundreds of fellow Irish across the States, we were having the summer of our lives. Not a day went by without some sort of excitement or weird and wonderful event transpiring. It was such a different experience to being at home. You were totally independent and had the type of freedom that wild animals enjoyed. I don't think I knew of one person who wasn't delirious about being on the Cape, and gaining some valuable experience and lessons of living in the big bad world. It was literally exhilarating.

Caddying was going well. The pay wasn't great but I was managing to get my name and face noticed by the members in the club. This was a help, especially for competitions, where the serious players would ask for you personally once they knew you were a decent caddy who could reliably give accurate information and advice and weren't just another commonplace bag carrier. This being said, most of the members only wanted the basic 'carry my bag and give me the club I ask for, otherwise be quiet and act as if you're a statue' routine. I could understand this sort of attitude towards the American caddies because they were all fairly young and ignorant of how the game should be played. But it was unforgivable behaviour in regard to the few Irish that were stuck among the rest of the plebs. We knew about the game and longed to act as proper caddies; helping them out with putts, club selection, distances – that sort of thing.

The one Irish guy who actually knew fuck all about the game, ended up winning caddy of the year at the end of the summer. Max was from Cork. He was over with a couple of friends from home. One of them, Bart, also caddied at the course. Bart had worked at The Old Head Of Kinsale Golf Club for numerous summers and could be regarded as an expert in the field.

Unfortunately for him and the rest of us, our responsibilities consisted of ball finding and bag handling. This, in particular, bothered Bart immensely; with his previous experience he hated being treated like one of the rest, and I, for one, couldn't blame him. (Bart hatched a devious plan to rob a couple of golf carts and drive them back to town; however, he had to leave early and the plot fizzled out).

Max and Bart lived out past the mall, which was a fair bit out of the way from Main Street. Their house had washing facilities and Internet use, which seemed a consolation prize for the location. Their landlord had recently sold a golf shop in Oosterville, which was about a ten-minute drive from town. He sold the lads a set of golf clubs each at a reasonable rate. I also bought a second-hand, forty-year old set of spanking new clubs – at least that's what it felt like as I was penniless at the time.

I made the journey out to his house when Max and Bart were lending a hand refurbishing the place. After picking out my favourite bag of sticks (that apparently had been around since the invention of the game) he kindly offered to deliver them to the Travel Inn so I wouldn't end up on either the stairway to heaven or the bungee jump to hell as I cycled down busy main streets with a bag of clubs balanced precariously on my back. They set me back $60 but it pretty much included everything you could possibly need in the game of golf from balls to gloves. I now had my weapons for the summer; it would have been a crime not to seize the opportunity of playing on this lavish course for free.

My first game in Hyannisport pitted me against the adequate skills of Bart, the master caddy from The Old Head. Max declined our invitation for a round because he couldn't tell the difference between a driver and a baseball bat. You could pretty much show up at the course any evening you wanted and be assured sunshine and a clear run till darkness fell about three hours later. After a fierce battle I managed to beat off Bart's challenge giving me a good start to my summer golfing career. Hopefully it would give me the confidence to do well in the end of season caddy competition. Only time would tell.

After the game, we went into the golf shop to ask the pro where we could store our bags. It turned out that we weren't important enough to be given even a couple of square feet where we could keep our golf clubs. I couldn't believe this. So much for treating your staff with a little bit of respect and dignity! Even telling him of our struggle trying to cycle all the way up here on a rickety old bike with a bag of clubs hanging from our shoulder had no effect. To me, that was the scabbiest thing I had ever heard. It wasn't as if they hadn't got the room to accommodate us. Bart decided to cart his bag home but I'd be fucked if I'd do the same. I stashed them around the back, behind a bush, until I could talk to Chad, the caddy master, about finding a place to stow them. It was too dangerous, not to mention exhausting, carrying them up and back to the course whenever you wanted to play a few holes.

The beach party season was well under way. Tens of us would head for the dunes every so often for a night of jarring and waterside fun. We would walk about a kilometre down the beach, which was called Kalmos beach, so it was impossible to see us from the places the police normally patrolled. We were well out of earshot, too. We would all bring a backpack filled to the brim with cheap cans of your choice and a CD player. So we could have either sweet harmonious tunes to drift away with or some rocking ballads if we were in a more upbeat mood. In the dark it was quite hard to see people and most of the time you never recognised whom you were talking to. But I don't think anyone cared as long as there was drink present on the sands of Kalmos.

One time as we partied in the darkness, I quickly became stoned. I was recovering from the flu at the time and I was taking tablets to help me recover. But there was a reaction from the alcohol, and after only a few beers I was for the birds. It was a really strange sort of feeling. I wasn't drunk, more like high. I lay down on the sand and started to relax and fall asleep. Every now and then, Nevaeh or Michael would come over and kick me to wake me, or at least I think it was them. For all I knew it could have been a beach bum who had come over to rob my stash of ale. When it was over, Michael helped me up and said it was time to go home. For the next five or ten minutes we engaged in a rugby tackling war (Drug-head got a bit carried away, but couldn't control himself) as we slowly walked back to the road. It was lucky I had Michael there to guide me home otherwise I may have been arrested or swept out to sea as I slept on the beach in my brainless state.

On another occasion, two of Nevaeh's friends from home came down from Boston for the night. We decided to throw a beach party in their honour. It was a seriously class night and in the end two of the lads picked up Laoibhse and Maria and catapulted them into the sea, drenching them from head to toe. As expected, everyone joined in the fun and games and we spent half an hour flinging each other under the warm, salty water. The sun had spent the day heating the ocean and it felt like you were having a bath in your own home; all that was missing were the Radox bubbles. In the end, no one wanted to get out; mental note: must invent floating beds.

On the way back, we took off all our clothes, apart from our underwear, and ambled down the middle of the road. As we passed different houses on the way back to the motel, Nevaeh spotted a huge American flag nailed to one of them. Her Boston friend legged it over and ripped it off the house, and we all scuttled away down the street. Thankfully no one spotted our transgression from any of the neighbouring homes, otherwise, we may have gotten a serious hiding.

The Americans are very uncompromising when it comes to their nationality and symbols of their free and treasured land. Every flag we took (and there were quite a few) was hung proudly on the walls creating the ultimate Irish-American house (the police suspected the Irish were connected with the disappearance of American flags and searched some of the houses; however, we managed to escape the warrant-free investigations). That night was unforgettable, a precious memory given to us by the Cape, which will be forever in our minds.

Sunday came and it was our last Pufferbellies before moving on to a different home, or at least, a traditional home. Every week, all the Irish were turning up in their best rigouts for a classic night of Pufferbellies magic. The only people who didn't go or didn't enjoy the place were Jessica and Clodagh. They didn't see what the rest of us saw, and chose instead to enlarge their bank balances on those evenings.

It was like a calling, nobody wanted to miss a Sunday night in this great establishment. Regret was felt if circumstances forced you to go without your weekly dose. We had made that night our own. It was like being in your local pub at home on a Friday night, everyone knew each other.

We had even formed end-of-night traditions by breaking out into a drunken choir and singing, *Beautiful Day*, by arguably the best rock band in the world, while forming a massive interlocking circle of bodies on the dance floor. Straight after that we sang the best rendition we could muster of our national anthem. It was the same every week. Even the Americans who were in the club stopped everything and listened in awe as we sprang to voice (well okay, maybe they were genuinely scared and horrified at our singing attempts but at least they acted as our audience).

These nights really helped the Irish to bond and interact. That night was an important factor in helping to make the summer what it was in the eyes of many a person. May the sweet taste of the jar be forever on your lips, Mocha.

Michael and myself were getting in scot-free every Sunday night as we had started to build up a good relationship with Mocha. As he was in charge, the majority of the time he was firmly planted at the door keeping abreast of things. He was beginning to have problems with his girlfriend, who worked on the door taking money, and they were arguing and fighting more frequently of late.

That night, Julie, the Irish girl who helped the Travel Inn to run smoothly, tried to work her feminine charms on me. I would say this was down to a not-so-little intake of the old, Dutch courage. As nice as she was, I wasn't really attracted to her. We chatted for a while and at the end of the night I ended up walking her home to Pleasant Street where she lived. When we got there, she turned around and asked if I'd like to come in. Knowing what this would result in, I told her 'no' as platonically as I could. I felt bad that I couldn't return her feelings but it would have caused more problems had I gone inside with her.

The day had finally come. We could at last move into a proper house that we could call home. Nearly a month and a half after arriving in Cape Cod and we had secured our own place. This was, at the very least, a day worth celebrating. As we found out, finding a place for nine people to stay was extremely difficult, if not impossible. We were rapturous and so thankful for our new abode. For all the times we had turned down the different shit holes that we looked at, it had now paid off.

We were the proud owners of probably the best dwelling of any of the Irish students staying on the Cape. Its location was one of her best traits. She was snuggled in halfway down Ocean Street, two minutes walk from the beach and five minutes walk from Main Street. This was perfect as the bulk of the Irish had to walk or cycle past our house on the way to the beach. There was never a shortage of people to flight a 'Beckham-pass' with Michael's gold football. (Mr Miagi would have been visibly smug when the ball became lodged at the top of the massive tree that stood in the garden for days). There must have been around eight or ten Irish houses along the street, which added to the appeal and uniqueness of the area.

Michael, Jack and I had to make ourselves scarce for most of the day. The landlady had said that she would be calling early and who knew what time she'd leave. That wasn't cause for concern as I was caddying and Jack was landscaping. So Michael was the only one who had to skidaddle (she'd never find him in the pub, would she?). I arrived at the house in the late afternoon. There were loads of bikes parked outside so I figured we were in the clear.

The house was unreal. It had two floors. There was one bedroom downstairs and two upstairs. The sitting room was bright and cosy. There were two couches and one single armchair. They were so comfortable, they should have occupied a spot in the middle of the mall where they could make some money from people paying to relax in them. We had a good-sized TV and video, all in one. The TV had about seventy channels so we were never stuck for something to watch (even if there was more time allocated to ads than actual programmes).

On the shelves, over the fireplace, lay ornaments and, in particular, a large handmade boat that looked fairly expensive. Not being able to trust ourselves, especially in the throes of drink-riddled activities, we took down the different statuettes, including the boat, and put them away in a closet until we were ready to leave at the end of the summer. With this done, there was no fear of any costly accidents happening so we could booze and party to our hearts' content.

The house was open plan, with no doors leading to the kitchen or dining room. Moving into the kitchen, it was small enough but that didn't bother us. There were no Jamie Oliver's in the group who wanted to prepare eye-catching, tongue-tickling, belly-busting banquets – unless the banquets consisted of hills of toast and not much else. The main thing was that it had a big fridge that could store and chill all our precious cans of beer and our large containers of orange juice, which mixed so well with our paint-stripping vodka.

Behind the kitchen was the dining room. A wooden table that could seat about six or seven people adorned the room. This was to be the party game room, which would host the different alcohol-fuelled Olympic Games that would keep us entertained through the long nights. Straight across from this was the lone bedroom on the ground floor. It was pretty small with just a single bed and a wardrobe.

Upstairs, on the left, was a small room with a double bed. This room was smaller than its counterpart below and the bed basically filled the room. The wardrobes were outside in the landing where your stuff could be kept. It was decided (amidst great debate and a little groaning) that Jack and Alyssa would sleep in the upstairs bedroom while Michael and Emma would inhabit the single bed downstairs. Although this may seem an unfair trade-off for the latter, it was the only room with a door and ultimately provided a bit of privacy. The other room had to be satisfied with a thin sheet for a door. At the end of the day this didn't provide any sort of privacy for a couple in love and didn't shut out the noise that was being created from below.

The last bedroom could easily swallow the other two, with enough left over to have a go at the couch. It had a bathroom and a double bed along with sufficient storage space for clothes and valuables. The remaining four girls claimed this room. Two blow-up beds could be bought and put on the floor, and sleeping arrangements could be rotated every night so that everyone got an opportunity to sleep in the bed.

For the time being, I was the only person without a place to sleep. We were also jubilant with the services of a washing machine and dryer. Now we didn't have to lug our clothes to town; change countless dollar notes into handfuls of quarters; wait for two hours; then cycle with them on your back sweating so profusely that when you arrived home you had to change on account of breaking the legal stench limit.

We well and truly broke the house in. We threw a special hullabaloo to warm her up for future sessions. We invited all the gang from Cork and Mayo and whoever else happened to be in the neighbourhood. Bono was to miss out on all the fun and frolics, as he had to return home for an interview about a job he had applied for before coming over. He was heartbroken at the sudden end to his time in America, and Maria, his lovely girlfriend, wasn't exactly dancing from the rafters either. It was such a pity he couldn't have stayed until the next day. But that's life for ya.

Al began a tradition, which would stand the test of time, of dreaming up some great party games to play. One sure thing was that if you participated in these games you would end up stumbling around the house, or possibly the street, a few hours into the night, and would be sure to be suffering from some sort of unpleasant ailment the next morning. The only downside to living here was that a nurse was living in the granny flat at the side of the house. She would be sure to send word to the landlady if our shenanigans were to get out of hand.

After partaking in Al's drink-filled entertainments, I didn't care where I slept that first night. So I made one of the couches my own, and slept the sleep of the devil-may-care.

Others were also as lucky as ourselves. Nevaeh and Clare moved into a house not too far from ours on Ocean Street. They shacked up with an English girl we had known from the get go, and three gregarious girls from Dublin. The three girls, Maggie, Bianca and Susie had come over together and had originally stayed in the

Best Value Inn with us at the start. It was a toss up between the three as to which one had the biggest boobs on the Cape. Their house was a kip but had a certain character to it. The girls didn't really care what it had; they had a place to live which worked out a lot cheaper than the motel.

The Cork lads all had to camp in one room back in the Travel Inn as they couldn't afford two. This meant a room made for four now had seven living in it. They offered to stage the Twister championships in the room, but funding and sexuality problems arose. Despite this, most of them stayed in our house, either on the chairs or on the floor. They couldn't be bothered cycling back to the motel after a night on the beer in the new homestead. They became part of the furniture. In the mornings, when I got up for caddying, they were always there, sprawled out on whatever they could get their hands on. The sounds of drunk snoring would set me up for the day; otherwise I felt something was missing. The sight of Deco half hanging off the armchair with his tongue rolled out like Pluto on drugs was a comfort to me, and helped me to face what lay ahead.

Matilda and Jeanie, too, had managed to find a home. Apparently it was quite nice. The girls had invited us up a few times but for some reason we had never found the time to visit. A friend from home had now joined them and they were all living together. Jeanie had been fired in the end from her job in the Chinese restaurant, much to her satisfaction. So she joined her best friend working in Schooners. I think if she saw one more grain of fried rice she would have dunked the plate over some snooty customer's head along with a portion of Peking sauce. Then she would have run down Main Street with that maniacal laugh often portrayed by the evil and slightly crazy villain.

It was good they let her go.

The gym was proving to be worth every penny Michael and myself paid for membership. We spent three or four days a week working out, counteracting the vicious McDonald's fat invasion. The gym was in the Radisson Hotel, not far from ye old liquor store. The lifeguard working at the pool was an Irish girl, a job that seemed to entail very little work, which gave her some time for leisurely hobbies such as catching up on her reading.

The main receptionist was a bit greasy, and asked Michael and I to set him up with some Irish girls. With no intentions of doing so, we, nevertheless, told him of a house party on Sunday night – that was a Tuesday. The next Monday afternoon we stopped by for an hour's workout. He bluntly groaned that he hadn't been invited to the party. We told him that it wasn't on and he replied.

'I know it wasn't on because you didn't invite me.'

He didn't seem to comprehend that no party actually took place. With that I said, as clearly as I could, in front of a few members who were exhaustedly leaning on the counter, that he didn't get an invite because:

'NO PARTY ACTUALLY TOOK PLACE!'

They sniggered and giggled and he turned a cherry red as he finally copped on to what we were trying to tell him.

'Oh,' he replied timidly.

The gym also provided flashes of entertainment that made it worthwhile. Once, Michael stood beside me encouraging me to blast out the last couple of reps on the leg press, and as I forced my legs to beat the weight, out of nowhere I almost crippled myself with the fart of the century. With the immense pressure and effort I was exerting, plus all those non-slimming meals, it was all too much. The shockwave reverberated across the room almost shaking the foundations of the entire hotel, like the aftermath of the Hiroshima bomb. We broke out in chinks of laughter as the smell began to spread and linger. A guy who was working-out on the other side of the room came over and asked if I was okay, clearly worried that something may have been wrong with me.

Another time we walked by one of the biggest black dudes we had ever seen. We were sure there was a body on the muscles somewhere. Just looking at him made your stomach ache and your own muscles run for cover. He was beating out reps with a bar that had such tiny weights at either end that even my granny could make look easy. I felt compelled to comment on what we were witnessing. I said to the Mr T look-alike that surely he could lift more than that. Michael thought we were done for. Thankfully, the biggest man in the gym saw the funny side of my cheeky slag, and refrained from using his tree-trunk thighs to pop my head.

One evening, shortly after moving into 327 Ocean Street, I was playing a round of golf at the course. I had started out with one of the members but he left soon after to attend a party. I decided to carry on. There was just something so relaxing about being out in the quiet of the evening with just your own thoughts to ponder. I still thought often of my ex-girlfriend, and in many ways I wished she was with me. I missed her. But then I realised I was making a success of the summer on my own. I was making loads of new friends and having the time of my life. It was a once in a lifetime experience and I was letting thoughts of a girl that I hadn't seen in nearly a year interfere with my enjoyment of Cape Cod. I came to a full and sober decision that I would forget about thinking about her, and let the summer work its magic on me to the fullest extent. We were over and it was buried deep in the past, so there was little point keeping her in my mind.

And that's what I did. I left her in the past.

As I walked down the stony path that led from the fifteenth green to the sixteenth tee box, with a clear and worry-free conscience, I came face to face with a deadly foe. Sauntering along, thinking about the many wonderful experiences I already had that summer, I raised my head and, there, in front of me, about 40 yards away, stood a very intimidating figure. It was a coyote. I stopped dead in my tracks, frozen.

Then it hit me. Animals can sense fear and are just waiting to exploit it. Realising this, I slowly but confidently started to walk towards the beast. He turned around and took a few paces, but then turned again to face me. I took out my nine iron. This was my favourite club in the bag so I figured I would be naturally gifted at using it as I attempted to slay my enemy, if it came to that. It didn't. The imposing character stepped off the path onto the marsh, and sidestepped me. He must have heard about my ability to wield a nine iron similar to the way one of the musketeers negotiates his sword.

I heard, later, that coyotes would only attack if they were in a pack. Lucky for him he wasn't cause I was feeling pretty mean. When I got home the first thing I did was change my underwear.

Just before we moved out of the Travel Inn we were told by Jackie, who was Jeanie and Matilda's friend, that there was a vacancy for a bus boy in the Ocean Grill. This was the restaurant part of the Blue Room. Jackie, who had come from Australia after travelling between different exotic locations for twelve months, didn't have a social security card. Ingeniously she used Jeanie's number and subsequently adopted her name while she was working there. The boss and all the employees had no idea of her scam, and she worked there for the whole summer under her friend's alias. Her cover was nearly blown one day when someone (and I'm not saying who this person was) addressed her by her proper name and not her work name (wasn't me).

Since I already had the job I'd always wanted (it's great being treated like rubbish and looking for the balls of uncoordinated planks for half the day in thirty-degree heat), Michael was the obvious candidate. He applied for it, and voila, he was the Cape's newest bus boy. It seemed to be a lucky move on his part because he received a tip of $20 from some woman he didn't even wait on. She found out he was from Ireland and that his surname was her surname and quickly went into a state of sheer happiness. She told him that they had to stick together and slipped a note into his hand.

Later on, when he looked at it, he couldn't believe that it was $20 – he was expecting a dollar or a couple at the most. To celebrate meeting his probably-not, distant relation, after work he went straight over to the liquor store and bought a 30-pack of Busch Light, which he would drink in her honour.

The next Blue Room on the agenda was a touch tragic. Jessica, Clodagh and the two girls had been drinking heavily back in their house in preparation for the three-hour dry patch. The drinks of the day were cocktails, but one person was to drink too much and would suffer the embarrassment of her mistake.

When they arrived, it was obvious they were well oiled. Ann Marie, their friend from home, was stumbling all over the place and literally fell on top of me as I sat on the armchairs I was so fond of. She was beyond drunk and probably didn't even know she was in Cape Cod never mind the Blue Room. After a short while her head spun round and she vomited all over the ground. She literally pucked-up a bucket of sick, and it wasn't one of those small beach buckets you'd buy on holidays. It was priceless to see how fast everyone jumped out of the way. The Americans were outraged and horrified at this hurl-a-rama and made sure to make their objections heard.

'Oh that's disgusting!' and, 'get her out of here!' comments flew from one yank to the next.

The Irish just looked over.

'Ah jasus, the poor girl, she must have sunk one too many,' and went back to their pints.

That part of the club suddenly got quieter for some reason.

After that the girls brought Ann Marie outside, but there was some confusion as to who was bringing her home. She threw a hissy-fit and made off down the street on her own. The girls didn't know where she had gone when they arrived home, she wasn't there. She had unwittingly leapt into some guy's car and apparently went to a party with him to a place she couldn't remember. She was lucky to arrive home safe and unhurt.

The following day I went to my old place of employment for my favourite lunch – a small meatball sub without fries (I could never afford the extra sixty-cent). One of the lad's friends or relations was working in the deli with them. They must not have been able to cope without my basic assistance so they hired her. The mad sister asked me if she could have a picture with the both of us in it. She said she was going to put it over the cash register, so who was I to say no (though having my mug over the register would no doubt scare many customers away). Her friend got the camera ready while she put her arm around me and made a come-to-bed-with-me-now smile. I didn't mind posing for a picture but sleeping with her was totally out of the question.

Once that was done, I was given my beautiful sub, and the words every skint Irishman wants to hear.

'Ah don't worry, there is no charge for that.'

I was starting to have second thoughts about giving her my body. I was on the verge of making her an indecent proposal – my body whenever you want it, in return for subs and fries whenever I want. But I just couldn't picture myself waking up beside her not-so-wholesome face after doing the dirt on my principles. I decided against and chose instead to savour my free meatball sub.

Later, Ann Marie would gain sweet revenge on Jessica, who literally took the piss out of her all day after the incident in the Blue Room. They invited me over for some cocktails and I was delighted to head on out for some icy strawberry daiquiri's. For some reason I couldn't drink very fast that evening, while Jessica was chugging hers back thinking she was a robot. She continued to slag Ann Marie and referred repeatedly to her tolerance level when it came to drinking.

Without an hour passing, Jessica stood up and went to the bathroom, and then wobbled into her bedroom. I went in to see if she was all right. She lay sprawled on the bed. I asked her how she was. With that, she got sick all over herself and the bed. I held her head and called Clodagh to give me a hand. Clodagh told me she could handle it from there. So I headed home, looking forward to the morning, when I would be able to call over and give Jessica the nihilistic mocking she deserved.

Not such an appetising White Russian

We were settling nicely into our new pad. I was sleeping on the floor beside Michael and Emma, who had taken over the single bed. It wasn't exactly the ideal arrangement for any of us, but was the best we could come up with. We agreed that whenever they wanted a couple of hours of intimate-time, it was theirs for the taking as long as my bedspread on the floor wasn't in the line of fire. I needed to sleep in a room that had a bit of silence. I was getting up at half five a lot of mornings so I needed a good three or four hours' beauty sleep.

We were having AA (absorbing alcohol) meetings every night without fail. They were discreet, though, as we didn't want to irritate the nurse living next to us by making too much noise. It was so easy-going. The Cork lads came over whenever they wanted, people drank whenever they pleased (which was most of the time) and everyone just did as they desired.

Michael and Emma were still distant. Their relationship just didn't seem to be able to cope with the stresses and strains America was creating. The tension was palpable between them, and Emma spent many occasions crying at the way things were unfolding. This wasn't what she envisaged before they came over.

One evening, as Emma was going through the emotions, Nevaeh grabbed her and dragged her out to Christy's. They ended up persuading some innocent bystander to buy them donuts and bagels as they were stone broke. This, at least, kept the sorrow she was feeling at bay as she doubled over in fits of laughter at Nevaeh's hilarious carrying on.

The other newly formed partnerships were still going strong and couldn't seem to get enough of each other. Sheila managed to work her way fairly skilfully through three of the guys from Cork. She was expecting her boyfriend from home to arrive during the first part of August. Despite this, she had a soft spot for Roy, and they were indulging in a sort of casual relationship.

It's a hard thing to practise abstinence when you are so free and living a life so different to the one you're used to. The thought of a partner at home sometimes isn't enough to defer you from being with someone you are really getting on with, someone you relate to. It's not that you have some sort of morbid desire to hurt your lover who is thousands of miles away across the Atlantic. You are living a new life and it's natural to want someone with whom you can share and experience it. An element of loneliness comes into play also, which can leave you pining for the security and comfort of another person. No one is perfect, and when feelings become too strong, it's hard to resist them.

Jack was busy working away at the old landscaping. I was employed for three days by the staffing agency to help out because they were short a couple of labourers. It was hard but extremely enjoyable work. When you fell out of Pat's car after arriving back to Hyannis you knew in your heart and soul that you had earned your few beers and slap-up feed at McDonalds. There was a certain amount of raw appreciation for the job, and a pride that you were actually making a difference. I'm sure Herbert felt this, too, as he sold another pink handbag to an overweight yank so she could carry her fluffy miniature pet poodle, named 'Poopyikins', dressed in a kilt, around the mall.

That work came just in time for me. The caddying had dried up like a river on the African Plains during the hot season, and my cash reserves weren't exactly overflowing either. Even the bank was starting to get a little worried about me. During that time (actually for the whole summer) my bank balance was smaller than one's privates after leaping into the Forty Foot in the snowy depths of winter. Caddying was sometimes scarce and often unpredictable. On a few occasions, I was down to my last cents, but each time that happened something emerged in the nick of time to get me out of trouble. In saying that I would have preferred a regular guaranteed income – less strain on the heartstrings.

Nevaeh was keeping the Cape entertained with her rambunctious behaviour. No matter when you bumped into her she always had a thoroughly unusual and fascinating story to tell. One evening, as the rest of us were dancing away in Pufferbellies, she was off with the American boyfriend of the English girl she was living with, and his friend. The three of them went back to the friend's house and spent the night swimming in his private swimming pool – not a bad way to spend your leisure time, it has to be said.

Another time she got hammered, and again, was flatly refused entry to the club. As she stumbled along the road she met a guy and went back to his place. Once there, she hopped into his bed and somehow managed to lose her shoes. She then made him walk her home, stopping along the way to pick up a drink and freshly-made bagel. She was impressively adept at getting what she wanted and would call on every bit of charm she had to do so. She was the self-proclaimed bagel queen of the Cape.

Pat and Caroline from the staffing company invited Jack, Michael and I for dinner in their house one weeknight. It was a sort of 'thank you' for the work we had done for them over the summer. The invitation was well received, it meant we wouldn't have to spend our hard earned money on food. Our plan was to eat as much as was humanly possible so we could live off it for a couple of days.

Dressed in our best gear (which for me was a pair of bleached jeans and a Heineken T-shirt) we crossed the street to where Pat was parked. The Northern Ireland lads, who were staying in the Travel Inn, were also invited. It was a short drive to the house, which was located outside Hyannis. It was a small, quaint place, where you felt at home, and like your typical Cape Cod house, made of wood. One of the guys and his girlfriend were actually living there for the summer. He did a lot of driving for Pat – picking people up and taking them to their jobs so it only made sense that he bunked there.

The other two guys had worked with us on July 4th at the Kennedy Compound. The pair of them were built like combat tanks, thanks to that ancient art of pumping iron. This held them in good stead, as, like

Jack, they were labourers. Only Garrett, who was the smaller of the two, kept up the weight training during the holiday months. He was a member of Gold's Gym where Michael and I worked out. Garrett, fair play to him, managed to keep faithful and loyal to his training. He was severe with his diet and continued taking protein shakes throughout, not wanting to become too sloppy and soft. With every sort of temptation just waiting to be devoured it was tough to stay with a regime such as this one.

Brian, on the other hand, wasn't as dedicated to the cause. He was a big lump of a man, a fella that you'd love to have on your side if a street fight broke out. I worked side by side with him during my three days' landscaping and we spent the majority of the time doing tasteful impressions of Arnie, with gems such as, 'Get Out!' and, 'She'll be back'.

We sat down to dinner shortly after arriving, and filled up on tasty fresh bread and butter as starters. For the main course we dove into huge trays of delicious lasagne. It was a meal fit for Lords – just a pity it was wasted on seven dozy Irish lads. How and ever we stuffed our faces until it was physically impossible to squeeze another morsel of food into our mouths.

Accompanying the meal we had homemade lemonade, one of Caroline's specialties. Once I tasted this orgasmic-juice I was hooked. The other lads didn't really like it as it was very sweet, but sweetness was my middle name (I changed it from Joseph when I was eighteen), and I was going to make sure none of it was wasted. After either three or four tall glasses of this mighty beverage I was as high as a kite – the sugar had gone straight to my head. It felt like I was floating on thin air and I giggled like a schoolgirl who had her first crush. Well, I had to make up for the absence of alcohol somehow.

We had all just about managed to hold down the feast, and it was time to get off home. Getting up from the chairs was no easy task. Caroline had treated us to a magnificent homemade meal and we had returned the favour by supplying gut-wrenching homemade wit and tales from the old country. Caroline wrapped up the last remains of dinner so we could take it home and give the girls some. She also gave me a big, chunky bottle of that rocket juice I had been drinking all evening to bring home. It had been a great supper and our first real decent meal of the summer cooked by caring hands.

Every night was like a party night on the Cape. It was very seldom that we didn't have some sort of get-together, whether it was a rip-roaring party or a more intimate affair with close friends enjoying a few frosties. One could never be certain who would turn up. Any one of the nine who were permanent residents in the house, or the seven who were semi-permanent, could invite someone new over for a drink, and they often did.

On one occasion, as Michael worked bussing tables, he met three girls from Boston. They chatted every time he went to their table and when they were about to leave he suggested, if they weren't doing anything that night, they should swing by for a jar. They took Michael up on this, and after searching for the house for about forty minutes they arrived. One of the other girls had also invited some guys back from work that same evening so it turned out to be a very lively night.

Michael and I were friendly with one of the young guys who worked in the liquor store (that wasn't hard given the amount of time we spent in there). He became a regular visitor, and, more often than not, he brought a couple of friends over as well. They were quite shy, but always managed to crawl out of their shells after ingesting some Dutch courage. They were more interested in smoking pot, though, than drinking, which meant that between us we had the perfect combination of narcotics and drink for a tranquil night in.

The main going-out nights were Sunday, Wednesday, and towards the end of July we discovered Kendrick's for a Thursday night. They weren't exactly your normal club nights at home in Ireland, but the majority of people tried to schedule their work shifts around them. No one really cared about having to work on a Friday or Saturday, as these were considered more weekday nights than anything else. Those three evenings had a habit of lasting until dawn and beyond.

Every Sunday after Pufferbellies one of the Irish houses threw a party which most people ended up attending. There were ten guys living in the house, five from Dublin and five from Cork. It was typical of the way things were over there, Cork integrating with Dublin and vice versa. If you had told the respecting counties of this trend before the summer, most would not have believed it. But it was the way things should have been.

The first time I was there was with Michael and Roy. We were sitting down chatting away and I had my feet up on a rotting wooden table. One of the guys who lived there wanted to pass and told me to get my feet down. This I would have done, if there had been no other way of getting around me. He could easily have walked round the other side of the miniature table. He wanted to show his superiority by making me take my feet down. Stubbornly I refused and said that I was comfortable sitting like that. With a face that would make a baby wail, he walked by the other side. He went over to his friends and told on me. Spiteful and cowardly, I know, but that's what the little girl did.

The next thing he and two of his friends came over and used the excuse that they wanted to pass in order to try and get me to take my feet down. I really did think this fascination with dominance was getting a bit ridiculous. I declined to remove my feet. This denial put things over the edge and they tried to remove my legs by force from the table. Tempers flared, and I warned them not to try that again. With that the whole lot of them stormed over and were followed by a very imposing giant of a Russian. I think he must have been a bodyguard or sparring partner to Arnie because he was enormous.

I quickly had a flash glimpse of what the future would be like if I was to take him on and it didn't look pretty. All my family and friends stood around my grave as my coffin was being lowered into the damp earth that housed what remained of my body. I think even if Brian and Garrett had have been there, and we had combined all our strengths, the mighty Russian would still have squashed us like cockroaches. With this prophecy leaning heavily on my mind, I gracefully let all thoughts of a fight slip and happily let them throw me out, relieved in the knowledge that my body was still in one piece.

Michael and I weren't bothered at being barred from the Nantucket Street house. There were bad vibes from the place anyway. It's hard to explain but the guys we talked to about it agreed, whereas most of the girls, for some reason, seemed to love going there. We felt intimidated by the house and just didn't feel comfortable there. So it was no skin off our noses when our mug shots went up over the door informing everyone of our expulsion.

Pufferbellies was always eventful and consistently entertaining. It never failed to provide a night filled with laughter and enough talking points to create a successful soap.

I was told by Jessica's friend, Rebecca, that Renee, who worked with her in the same restaurant, fancied me. This surprised me, as I hadn't noticed any signals whatsoever. If I had any trouble believing this, I certainly did that week in the club. From the very start of the night, Renee's friends did the best job they could conveying to me her feelings. All night they told of what she felt for me, and how I should go over and talk to her. This persistent harassment bordered on stalking. The whole thing came as a total surprise and I was being nagged to the point of insanity. It was like my mother (sorry mam) insisting that I clean my room. When I get nagged I have a habit of becoming obstinate and tend to stick my heels in.

They were saying things like, 'ah she's shy, go over and tell her you like her' and, 'just go and give her a kiss'. It was like being in primary school again when you got your friends to ask someone you like to be with you. I thought we had gone past that immature stage long ago and refused their suggestions outright. It's not as if this girl needed that sort of petty assistance from her diehard friends, she was well able to talk for herself. She was also very pretty. It wasn't as if I was going to turn her down for looking like she got hit in the face with a frying pan condemning her to a life of pure ugliness. There was no reason for her friends to badger me like this, and instead of convincing me to do what they wanted, it turned me off the idea altogether.

As the night ended, their pleas and arguments kept flying in my direction. I saw Nevaeh standing to the side of me. I yelled over to her and asked if she wanted to go and get a bagel. Suddenly, all the moaning yobs shot their heads round and glared at her. With a hesitant smile, as I think she thought she was going to be lynched by the bloodthirsty pack in front of her, she timidly said.

'Yes.'

I grabbed her and we made a run for the exit. With great relief we reached the street outside but continued running and never looked back. (The cheesy bagel was delicious and was without doubt the highlight of the night).

Everyone was getting their own unique experiences and learning their own lessons from the summer. Some found comfort in work, while others played as hard as they could. Some went to achieve certain personal goals, while others were lost in the splendid world of all that was new and exciting. There were no set rules or conformist ideas, everything went and all was tried. People ate dinner at different times, times that suited them, as very few people worked the same hours. You were caught up in the middle of hundreds of similar folk as yourself, but you were different, and you pursued your own plan and desires. You drank when you wanted, went cycling when you wanted, had sex when you wanted, smoked when you wanted – over there you were your own individual person and lived the summer whatever way you saw fit.

Jessica and Clodagh were particularly fond of the hard-playing part. Work was good for them. Tips were coming in thick and fast. They could afford to relax to the extent that they worked and enjoy themselves to the limit. There was a period from the start of July till the beginning of August when I didn't see them at all. This was the classic example of the summer pulling people in different directions. While they were off at different house parties I'd be having a quiet night in, so I would be able to get up the next morning to caddy and ensure my survival.

This was the accepted norm in Cape Cod. When you got the chance to see people, it was great and the craic was had. But when you disappeared for certain portions of time people knew you were working, so they in turn went out with other people and so the circle was complete. Even though it was a holiday situation, at the end of the day you still had to bring home the bread and peanut butter.

Nevaeh and Clare's notable exclusion from many of our house parties was understood and sympathised with. They were normally fairly good at attending work on a regular basis, apart from the odd fake 'sickie' when the activities from the night before took their toll, or when there was something too good to miss that they had to call in ill. The two girls really knew how to liven a party (except when Clare fell asleep in the sitting room after drinking too much, but the snoring was funny) and were sorely missed when work snatched them away for the night.

Michael's responsibilities were increased by his manager when he saw how capable he had become. He was now performing lunch-hour shifts as a waiter and evenings as a bus boy. Nervous at first, but after a short spell of adjustment he was a natural at it. The restaurant was impressed with his people skills and knew it would be a good move to promote him to waiter status. Michael's charming and outgoing personality only heightened the boss's pleasure at his new-found emerald. There were evenings when Michael would be caught up with work and was late for parties. But he knew more than most how to enjoy himself, and once he was finished, threw himself head first and mouth open into the festivities.

The girls in the house were all employed in the Duck, apart from Alyssa, who, luckily for her, was working alongside Herbert. Their shift times were always different, so sometimes they couldn't make certain club nights or were late for some functions. They all made it home eventually, though, when they well and truly let their hair down.

Maria was able to party and drink with the best of them, and was in her element as the night came alive. Every time Sheila drank she became all, lovable, and the world was a big, happy paradise. That only lasted until the morning, of course, when she would come down the stairs with a throbbing head and sunken face. Alyssa liked to spend time with Jack as both of them were earning semi-decent money now. They could afford regular trips to the cinema and the odd meal out here and there. As they both worked quite early, they would retire to bed as things were beginning to liven up. They joined the rest of us for mad nights when they didn't have the burden of work the next day.

Our cousins from Cork were taking it easy with the energy exertion. John was the only real hard worker out of the lot of them. He was keeping Bike Zone ticking over, and he never missed a party. He was the quieter, more refined type of chap, but in saying that never turned away anything of what you might call, alluring consequence.

This changed in July. Deco and Jacob were offered jobs in the local airport, just down from the mall. Jacob had worked there the previous year so it was a nice connection to have. They had to get up earlier than Jack and myself. When they were halfway through their day, it was breakfast time in the Travel Inn, so it was back there for a mid-morning feed during their break. This was sweet as it meant they saved money on food and for the first three weeks was especially appreciated – there was a delay with their social security cards and until the airline was presented with these the lads didn't get paid. Deco ended up owing a lot of money to a lot of people.

As for Al, his job consisted of organising the most frenzied drinking games known to man and we deeply respected his chosen occupation. Roy had only meant to come over for a holiday but soon postponed his flight date when he experienced the place for himself. He couldn't get enough and certainly wasn't going to go home as long as he could afford to stay.

Bono, who had returned home since, also decided to become a member on the cashless dole. In the light of his mother's wrath, I hereby declare that he tried very hard to find a suitable job and was very unlucky not to get his hands on one. Though I did try and tell him that it would be hard to find a job in bed with Maria or downing shots in the party room (don't worry Bono, your secret is safe with me, she'll never suspect a thing).

As time rolled by Michael and I struck up a great friendship with Mocha, the radio DJ. We started spending more time with him and he often invited us up to his house for a few Red Bull and vodkas. Luckily for him he got the Red Bull free from one of his contacts because we were drinking them faster than a health freak drinks water. It was a twenty-minute cycle up the hill from town but there was some marvellous scenery along the way.

His girlfriend was there on most occasions, though the rift between them seemed to be growing wider by the day. He had been with her for four years and it was tough on the pair of them. We'd go out to the course to play a few holes and have a chin wag before the night set in accompanied by his faithful dog and a couple of bottles of beer. It really was the life as you relaxed out on the green grass with the sight of the sun setting into the ocean, and the calming evening breeze gently lapping over you. Feeling totally at ease, we'd share a few glasses of the good stuff, listen to some of his new tunes, and then head on down to Pufferbellies.

I forgot to bring my passport with me one time. They let me in on the stipulation that I wasn't allowed to drink. That was grand as I had no money anyway – so what's new. I was up on the dance floor with Mocha. He had a Red Bull and vodka, which he didn't want anymore so he gave it to me. Without thinking I drank away at it. How was I to know that I was being spied on by undercover security guards. I was approached, detained and promptly evicted from the club. Mocha tried to tell them it was just Red Bull but they were having none of it. They must have realised I was Irish, and concluded that there must have been some sort of alcoholic substance in the glass. I was left to sit on the fence outside like an outcast. People kept coming up to me and asking why I wasn't inside and all they could do was laugh when I told them what happened.

I wasn't the only one the bouncers felt compelled to eject from the club. Matilda's Dad had come over to visit her, so she brought him to Pufferbellies to show him the culture in Cape Cod. Without a second thought the first thing he did was buy her a drink, as you would. Little did he know this place wasn't like Ireland. In no time, the both of them found themselves outside with Michael and I, who had come out to join me out of sympathy.

Two more girls that we had met a few nights beforehand were the next condemned contestants to join our new, elite club for misfits. Michael had brought a two-litre bottle of vodka and coke and had hidden it in our secret compartment under the branch. We had just as much fun chitchatting sitting on the curb outside the club and listening to the music that flowed out through the open doors. We were all in great spirits and the banter was massive between the six of us. Who needed to be in the club when we had a hard stone curb and a bottle of vodka at our disposal.

When you spend three months away with this many people, it's inevitable that you won't get on with everyone. Some people were going to have conflicting personalities and you just had to accept it.

The same was true for Laoibhse and myself. Shortly after we moved in, roughly eight of us sat out on the veranda at the back of the house. It was late at night and we were chatting and drinking without a care in the world. Behind us was thick marsh – a place you really didn't want to get drunk and fall into out of fear you would never again be seen. Nature was calling me at one point and I decided to walk down the eight steps that led you to the watery scrub and go there, as there was already someone in the toilet. As I carefully took each step as it came, Laoibhse asked in a critical tone of voice where I was going.

'To take a whiz.'

'You can't do that,' she said vehemently.

This made me smile and I repeated what I was going to do. With pent-up anger, and disgust on her face, she turned to the others and blasted how disgusting that was, loudly enough so I could hear, of course. Nevaeh, to my pleasant surprise, stuck up for me and commented that she should grow-up.

Personally I saw nothing wrong with this. I don't consider myself ultra-sophisticated – just a man of the land. What would she do if she was ever stranded on a desert island where there was no bathroom with a door and someone to dry her hands for her; hold it, I guess. There was notable tension between us in the house, which I'm sure people felt, but you can't be best buddies with everyone.

After one intensely heavy night's drinking in Kendrick's nightclub, I somehow managed to get at cockcrow and go caddying. And this was even after Michael and myself had polished off the cans we had hidden under a row of hedges down the road from the club afterwards. It was worthwhile making the effort to go to work because it was a particularly enlivening day's graft.

A married couple, playing with the mother-in-law, picked me to caddy. Halfway down the first fairway they realised I was from Ireland. Immediately they directed their attentions towards me and for nine holes asked every possible question under the sun, though they were mostly interested in our tradition of drinking. I told them stories about things that had happened to me back home and they were intrigued. They were your average, everyday tales. I thought it best to shield them from the, what you might call, 'better nights'.

So impressed were they that they wanted to introduce me to their eighteen-year old daughter. I think they had already started to plan where the wedding was going to be held and what type of finger food was going to be served. I was flattered. It was nice to be thought of like this, and if their daughter turned out to be drop-dead gorgeous then butterfly prawns would be my recommendation for the finger food. They had only time to play nine holes, so after the game was finished they bought me lunch and gave my employers a sparkling reference. They paid me handsomely, and about five minutes after they left, they returned with their family to introduce them to their favourite wee Irish caddy. I met their two youngest kids and the one and only single daughter. She wasn't half bad, and I told her if she ever wanted to come over to the house with a couple of friends for a few jars she was more than welcome (I was thinking of Deco sitting alone in his room without a girl, it just wasn't right).

That same week also saw me win my first honour as an aspiring caddy. There was a ladies doubles competition and the two women I caddied for ended up taking the prize by a clear margin (it must have been down to my extensive skills in the field, or might it have had something to do with them being two of the best female players in the club. My ego tells me to go with the former).

Bono surprised us all with an unexpected return to the Cape. He had attended the interview and secured the job, but they didn't need him to begin working for a while. His parents suggested that he go back to America for a week or so, as they saw how demoralised he was at being home. Almost as soon as he heard these words coming out of his parent's mouths his flights were booked and he was packing his sun cream once again.

Everyone was delighted to see him. It had only been a little over a week since his departure but it felt longer. We had all talked to him over the phone a few times, and Maria was over the moon with this unannounced pleasure. A party was deemed to be in order to celebrate the prodigal son's return. It was a lively night, the house was buzzing with people. The Northern Ireland lads came round and the funky fluids were flowing.

Brian and Laoibhse grew closer as the night went on. This was a rather bizarre pairing in that Laoibhse was sort of a feminist, who thought she was superior to any man. One time Alyssa was ironing Jack's shirt because they were late for a date. Laoibhse thought she was absurd, and said, loudly, that she would never iron anything for a man. I had to bite my tongue from reacting to such a barbed remark. I respected Alyssa for the way she ignored it and carried on the favour to her boyfriend. Brian was a man's man, and unlikely to let any girl walk over him. It was obvious they didn't really know each other, cause if they did, I reckon they would have stayed as far apart as Mars is from Venus. They wound up getting together and spent the night in one and other's arms sleeping on the couch.

Such bliss was never destined to last. The next night, Brian got all dressed up. According to Garrett he didn't normally do that for a girl. We all sat around the living room conversing on a variety of amusing topics. I was sitting in my normal armchair and Garrett, Brian and Jack were sitting on the couch to my right. Michael was plopped on the arm of my chair so for a good while I didn't know what was going on, on the other couch to the left of me. Brian seemed to be staring incessantly at the other side of the room. I glanced past Michael to see a half drunk Laoibhse lying on the chair with a grubby American who was shamelessly running his hands all over her.

I couldn't believe my eyes. It was going on right in front of the guy who had made a huge effort to impress her. Brian didn't take this well. As you can imagine it got to him more than it should have. The poor guy ended up drinking himself into a tizzy and then puked all over the couch and floor. It was funny to see how a girl could have such an effect on a seemingly macho, tough-man, but at the end of the day we are all human and emotions are easily touched. It was a good thing Bono came back because he was the only one brave enough to clean it up. If he hadn't have been there, I think the yellow, carrot-sprinkled puddle would have been left where it was, and we would have moved out when the smell became unbearable.

The weather towards the end of July had taken a turn for the worse. Most of the month had been so fine but now it was Mother Nature's chance to punish us for taking the sun for granted. We had nearly a week of torrential rain, which quickly suffocated my income line.

Out of desperation I went down to Helga, the weird lady we had met at the start, to ask about a job in the car park. A couple of the Cork lads, who had been working there, had since gone home. I no more wanted to work there than Laoibhse wanted to search for urinated soaked bodies in the nearby marsh pit, but something had to be done. Instead of working in Hyannis, she told me I would be going to Boston to work on her house the following week for three days. There were a couple of other lads travelling and our job would be to revamp the huge castle-like mansion for a mundane $8 an hour.

How lucky I was, I thought, as I strolled down the road after my brief chat with the local lunatic. I had to accept this degrading slave work as I was so broke. I even had to borrow $25 in order to pay the weekly rent (food has a habit of tasting a bit bland when you spend minus $25 on it). I didn't enjoy relying on other people like this and wasn't planning on making it a habit.

My situation wasn't helped when I had to throw out three white T-shirts because I couldn't for the life of me get the black stains that marred them to come off. The washing machines in America were only useless. They worked on a lower wattage and the water wasn't as hot as back home, so the clothes often came out little better than the state they went in. Like the moron I am, I didn't bring a lot of clothes with me in the first place, and with no loot to buy more, people were going to start noticing a more pungent smell around the house.

Thankfully it didn't come to this. Mocha, in his kindness to humanity, gave me three T-shirts he didn't need anymore. Ah, the smell of cleanliness. It was a guarantee that I wouldn't be booted out of McDonalds. No stink from me – no people running for the hills neglecting to purchase their Big Mac, or six.

During the week after we had been thrown out from Nantucket Street, we met one of the lads from the house in Kendrick's. He told Michael and I that we could come back any time we wanted, that it had just been a freak incident that caused the problem in the first place. This was decent of him and we told him his sentiments were appreciated and that we'd probably see him on Sunday night, dark and late. Sunday came and

Pufferbellies had ended, so we decided to give the house one more try.

Nevaeh, Michael and myself went up to the door. One of the lads was standing there like the protector of some sort of sacred refuge. He wouldn't let us in. We told him that one of his friends had said we would be welcome back. But he didn't budge an inch and with a slimy grin refused us once again. As we politely tried to reason with him, he tried to push me from the entrance, only to have his hands firmly slapped away.

One of his friends then came out to join him and they both caught me by the shirt. I wouldn't have minded only I liked that particular item of clothing, it happened to be my only going-out shirt. In retaliation, I grabbed the pair of them and sent them stumbling backwards with an effective shove. I was holding a can at the time and beer splattered over the three of us. This is it, I thought. I was expecting a massive onslaught, for them to come barging at me with fists flying, but nothing. I think the push earned me a bit of respect. As soon as that occurred the guy who said we were allowed in originally, came outside.

A minute later, we were strolling around the house with smiles as wide as Krusty the Clown's grin. Two minutes later, we were on the way out. We just didn't get good vibes from the place and decided to go home for a few quiet beers instead. The two guys weren't impressed at all by our antics and when we were leaving, they said.

'All that and you're going already.'

That was the sad reality I'm afraid. The place just didn't warrant our presence so we made tracks for home.

Back at our glorified estate, we were about to become foodless for a week. Days after moving into the house the cooker began leaking gas. The smell was something terrible. We felt light-headed even when we were standing out in the garden. We decided to call the fire brigade to come and check it for us. We weren't in the mood to get blown up; we had far too many gala evenings to attend.

I wasn't there when the suited guys came out to check our gas. They directed the lads not to use the cooker anymore. Ah well, out the window went my cheap pasta dinners! The girls insisted on having their photos taken with the hunky uniformed men of fire. Nevaeh took it a step further and tried to bag herself a date, while Michael went out and offered them a beer for their troubles. With the cooker now out of commission it left a few people with some minor headaches. I had been living on cheap boxes of pasta from the local supermarket and now I would be forced to eat out, leaving me to scrounge around looking for extra cents.

With the second month of our adventure just at an end, overall, things were going amazingly well apart from the odd niggle here and there which was to be expected. The only thing I could have wished for was to have been put in the higher income bracket, but even this was enjoyable in its own perverse way. There was a constant challenge, one that I was determined to overcome, and I knew it would teach me a lot of lessons for the future (including how to sniff out a McDonalds from five miles and how to wear the same pair of boxers for days on end without fainting from the smell).

The Irish Rover lives on

10

August dawned and the sun returned after its weeklong holiday abroad – probably to Ireland. Thoughts of travel and exploration were on the minds of just about everyone. The only drawback was the fact people were quite low on money, and personally, I hadn't two dimes to rub together. I fancied the idea of buying a two-week Amtrak rail pass, which allowed you go anywhere in America any time you liked. I would have to work like one or all of those seven dwarfs if I wanted to take this option, and the only way I was going to do that was if Snow White was waiting for me at the other end.

Michael and I couldn't afford the third month's gym membership. It was the only thing keeping us lean. Without it we had no way of burning off the extra calories from the many chicken burgers and double cheeseburgers we were scoffing. We had long ceased to buy chicken salads because they didn't fill us up enough for the money we were paying. We could get three burgers and two packets of peanuts for the same price – with a cent remaining. When you're hungry, this extra food goes a long way.

Bono left for the second time a day before August, no less upset and frustrated at missing the remainder of the summer as he was the original time. He and Maria spent the day in Boston before he left, wandering round the grounds of Harvard University. It was the last time they would see each other for about a month and a half, and they had become extremely close over the weeks spent out there. There were no conditions swapped or stipulations agreed upon. She was in America and he was in Ireland. If what they had was real, then it should be able to withstand pretty much anything, and when she returned home they would take up where they left off. When it was time to part for good, Bono couldn't quite hold back the tears as he watched Maria's bus drive back to the Cape, leaving him to make his way back to Cork, alone.

Jacob and Shauna, incidentally, were going home that same day for a week. One of Shauna's relations was getting married, so Jacob was faced with the daunting scenario of meeting all her family at once. They were able to make the round trip fairly cheaply as Jacob got flights for nothing working for the airline.

After a week the feckin' electrician finally showed his face at the house. We had rung the landlady a few of times about it, and we were slowly starving from lack of pasta. Michael and I were the only ones in the house that afternoon. He had an Irish surname and got a great kick out of talking about his Celtic roots with us. As it turned out, the right-hand side of the cooker was fucked and he told us only to use the left side when cooking. That was grand, we could get the pasta simmering once again.

The tank for the outside barbeque was low on gas so we took a chance asking him for a lift to the local garage to get it refilled. He was only too happy to bring us, and unknown to Michael and myself it was a good ten-minute drive to get it refuelled. When we got there the electrician went in to get someone and we stood at the pump with the cylinder waiting for gas. A guy of about nineteen that looked like Harry Potter came over and asked what we wanted. Michael and I looked at each other and smiled. He genuinely didn't know what we wanted. Michael made a funny comment that seemed to confuse Harry even more (wasn't Harry Potter meant to be smarter than that), so to put him out of his misery we asked him to fill the tank beside our feet with gas.

On the way back we asked for one more favour – a pit stop at the liquor store to pick up our normal order of a 30-pack of Busch. As a reward for his generosity Michael bought him a little bottle of Jameson so he could savour the taste of Ireland and imagine he was there.

One late evening in early August, after a club night, Michael and I ended up going back to Julie's house with a couple of her friends. We were all half buckled and for some reason there were a couple of American guys there, too – I was too inebriated to know why.

We proceeded to lead the guys into the intriguing world of Pokemon. We described how it had originated in Ireland; evil Leprechauns and seething fairies would fight to the death with rusty blades and mini-hammers. They were suspicious at first but as we created more and more in-depth stories we managed to convince them of our tall tale. We described how these characters would fight against wild animals in the forests of Ireland leaving trails of blood along the pine-covered ground. We told them other creative yarns along the way. In the end they were captivated by how mad the Irish were. After that, I ended up being with Julie out on the porch (so much for my earlier good intentions). It was only meant to be a bit of fun, but afterwards, she thought there was going to be more between us. But that wasn't what I wanted. Despite that, we remained friends and it didn't have any adverse affects on the rest of her man-hunting endeavours.

We all had begun to search for an alternative place to live for the duration of the week we had to vacate the house. It wasn't going to be hard getting somewhere to stay for seven days; it was just a hassle. All our bags had to be packed again. By now we had become experts in this area and even knew how to arrange our clothes in a proper order. The house would have to be clean and neat for the intruding visitors. We had to be gone on the ninth and would be able to return on the sixteenth. The only advantage in all this was the saving of $125 on rent, which would be a huge boost.

A day out was needed, so we decided to go cinema crawling. 'Operation Many Free Films' was planned out with intricate detail, taking every possible scenario into account. None of us had been to the cinema yet so it was about time we rectified that. We would turn up for the first movie at around twelve. Each of the features was approximately spaced out by two and a half hours. This was good timing to allow us jump from one film to another. It was all looking good for our dishonest adventure. All we needed now was supplies.

The first obstacle we encountered was the sign 'No Backpacks Allowed' nailed to the wall in the lobby as you entered the building. We looked at each other. Five backpacks hung guiltily from our shoulders. Trying to act as normal and innocent as possible, we each paid the $5 cover charge to see *T3*, which was scheduled to start in a few minutes. As we briskly walked past the food counter ignoring the checkout guys' puzzled faces as to why we weren't buying anything to eat or drink, we made our way onto the last challenge before we could relax in the security of the theatre: The Ticket Man.

This guy would frighten a sumo wrestler (obviously he took advantage of employee perks). If he noticed anything suspicious, he could escort us from the building and there would be nothing we could do. The thought of him falling on us would have made surrender obligatory. With great social grace and people skills, we managed to get by the colossal beast guarding the film area and stroll into T3. The danger had passed; we were home and dry.

Michael, Nevaeh, Clare, Bruce and myself settled in for the afternoon. Bruce was a caddy at the golf course, but had since found a job labouring instead. The money and stability had appealed to him. He lived at the top of Ocean Street in a large, arresting house. In his spare time, Bruce and the couple he was living with, who were friends of his from home in Limerick, worked at restoring the house. His best friend Eoin had to work extra hard. His girlfriend couldn't find a job so he ended up supporting both of them. What a drag.

The house needed a major facelift. So they helped by sanding the wood and painting it, improving the overall look and appearance of the garden by weeding, and planting flowers in their place. The dwelling overlooked the harbour presenting an aesthetically beautiful view. Bruce was a tall, strong chap who regularly worked out, and was a member of the gym where Mocha's girlfriend worked. He was firmly built and had arms like congregated steel poles – he and John had undoubtedly two of the best male bodies on the Cape. Yet despite his somewhat imposing presence he had been thrown out of Kendrick's the previous week for robbing mixers to add to his vodka. Even his formidable stature had to yield to bouncers who were bigger than him.

When the movie started the bags were opened. As this was going to be a long day we decided to bring the crucial items that everyone needs for a stint in the cinema. It starred such favourites as beer, vodka, fresh meatball subs, crisps and chocolate, with the occasional appearance from, a burger without a bap and a lunch box filled with recently expired pasta. I don't think Nevaeh needed much food as all her nourishment was coming from staring adoringly at Bruce's arms. She was a mighty fan of big strong arms and Bruce's babies were really getting her juices flowing. Beforehand, we had all made quick trips to the shop and liquor store to pick up some delicious supplements to accompany the films. The backpacks were filled to repel any hunger pangs.

After a thoroughly enjoyable first flick, we moved on to *Johnny English* to fill the void before the next major motion screening. After half an hour of insufferable shite it was time to hit *Pirates Of The Caribbean*. During the film Bruce drank a little too much vodka a little too quickly. He chatted away loudly, half pissed to Clare. It was damn annoying but comical at the same time. Our attempts to encourage him to keep his voice down fell on deaf ears. Clare was ready to stab him with a vodka bottle, though with the cut of him, it probably would have smashed into a thousand little pieces. I think he got tired after a while, and started to sober up towards the end. Another good movie it proved to be and if I was a girl I would definitely like Johnny Depp. The 'past-its-best-pasta' wasn't quite as satisfying, but to hell it with, it was on to our next viewing.

There was a gap of around an hour before our final blockbuster, *Bad Boys 2*, so we could dip in and catch most of another film. As we walked down the aisle we peered into a couple of theatres to see what was on, but they were empty. As we turned around to search the other side of the aisle, two security guards were walking our way. We had to be quick. Opening another door the room was, again, empty. Getting swiftly closer, I looked to my left and saw *Finding Nemo* currently being shown in the theatre.

'Ah sure there it is lads, that's the one were looking for.' I exclaimed loudly as the oncoming guards came within earshot.

Once in the doors, we dashed to the front seats. On the way was a step, which I didn't see, and nearly ended up falling onto Nevaeh as she led the speedy charge. Another close call but another well crafted escape. The fear and exhilaration ran through us like an electrical current. Who would have thought a day at the pictures could be so much fun.

It was time to face the aisle once again. We had just about caught the whole of *Finding Nemo*. Peeking out the door, it was all clear. All we had to do was make our way down the carpeted walkway and round the corner to our final destination. Success, we were in, we had avoided the attention of snooping party poopers. I was relieved because I wasn't sure if watching a film without paying constituted a bullet to the temple. The day was nicely rounded off by some violent action and hysterical moments. It did prove fatal to Bruce however as Nevaeh's attention had now switched to gawking at Will Smith's even more muscular limbs.

Ten and a half hours later it was time to go home for some quality sleeping – I mean drinking, silly me. As we made our way from the lobby out into the clement night air, one more decisive moment occurred that would properly seal the evening. Caught up in talking, because for the most part she had been mute as was demanded by the nature of the day, Nevaeh failed to see the metal beams that supported the doors in front of her. With a loud thud, she ploughed into the beam stopping her dead in her tracks. Slightly shaken and dazed, she laughed and walked on. It looked and sounded sore, but with the stubbornness of an ox she wiped her brow, strolled on, and didn't look back.

Max, the lucky fit bastard happened to be in the right place at the right time one afternoon. As he was working on his landlord's house, a couple of the landlord's friends came by. Max was a long distance runner, and often ran the distance to the golf club in the mornings. He was fairly strict with himself and continued training even in the energy-murdering humidity of the day.

He managed to get chatting to one of the guys, who, coincidently, was also a runner. This guy did landscaping work and he offered Max a peach of a job. Whenever he was needed, they would call him and pay him $20 for every hour he worked, all tax-free. Getting paid this in the States during the summer was the equivalent of being rich at home. Some days he would come up to me and boast coyly to my face that he had made over $500 in a particular week, while I was a step away from sleeping in the gutter. Max was now secure; he combined the two jobs and was never again stuck for money.

Though envious, I thought I could get my own back on him by annihilating him in pool. We played each other regularly in Pufferbellies. To my horror, he sailed over my challenge most of the time leaving me utterly humiliated. As a former semi-pro of the game I thought I would have no trouble in disposing of his meagre resistance. I should have stayed at home watching *The Fresh Prince Of Bel Air*. I thought I might even the score by taking him on in a race but I figured that might add insult to injury considering he had claimed first place in the Cape Cod Road Race.

So I let it be, and bowed my head.

Michael was living the life of Riley in the Ocean Grill. A fully-fledged waiter he had aspired to be, and the money flowed like vodka on a typical night in our house. He worked hard and was allowed only one full day off a week. But it was the most enjoyable job he had ever had. He looked forward to work in the late mornings. Most of the time he was groggy from the night before but he sweated this off fairly rapidly. He had somewhat of a cult status in the place. All the staff got on really well with him and the barman used to give him free cocktails whenever he liked. He was also playing soccer with the barman and his friends once a week, a short drive from Hyannis. He was entitled to get in free to the nightclub and was allowed have two people on his VIP guest-list who could also leave their wallets undisturbed.

Whenever I was cycling on Main Street I'd always stop by and see how he was doing. He would drop everything, including taking someone's order, and come over for a quick chat. Herbert would have been jealous of Michael's occupation as a waitress, and I'm sure would have let go of any handbag he was selling for the chance to don a flowery apron.

Perks came with most of the jobs. Deco and Jacob were no different. The boys could practically fly anywhere in the world for the price of a meal. Working for the airlines, all they had to do was pay the tax and they had the freedom of the skies. But that wasn't all though. Friends and family were given huge reductions as well and they made good use of this benefit. They would travel regularly to Boston and New York on day trips dragging delighted close friends along for the ride.

With just one more Pufferbellies and Blue Room before we left the house, we were determined to make them interesting. And interesting they certainly were. The previous week Irish Night had been cancelled to make way for Reggae Night. Don't ask me why because I couldn't tell ya. Maybe it was because the Jamaicans on the Cape were feeling excluded and this was an attempt to make them feel wanted. Pufferbellies was sorely missed that Sunday, but now it was back, bigger than ever.

The club was crammed. There would be only a few more Pufferbellies and people were making the most of the time left. It's quite a special thing to see people from different Irish counties talking away to each other and getting along, not so much as giving a thought as to where they were born. Everyone was equal, there were no better, just friends. Had there been any trouble with anyone, the Irish would have stuck up for each other and fought alongside one another. There was a closeness that didn't seem to exist at home. It was powerful, genuine, and inspiring. Amazingly there were no fights that I know of between any of the Irish during the three months there. People were there to enjoy themselves, to learn and to create friendships that would last. The diverse nature of the summer helped make it as special and memorable as it was.

The comedy rating of this particular Sunday night ranked high on the scale. Bart, Max's best friend, had somehow managed to lose his shoes as well as the shirt off his back. Half gee-eyed, he ventured out to the volleyball court for a drunken game. He removed his shoes and shirt, for fear of ruining them, before joining the fun. When he had finished playing his stuff had disappeared. Not giving a damn, he spent the night walking around half naked, happy as Larry. I'm sure if he was sober, he would have been fuming and gone around to every person quizzing them as to the whereabouts of his clothes. Bart was eventually thrown out. I don't think the bouncers appreciated his indecent exposure.

Bart wasn't the only casualty that night; Deco also bit the dust. I had a beer sitting on the table and Deco wanted a mouthful. I was only too happy to provide him with some refreshment. He took a gulp but was spotted by one of the eagle-eyed giants that roamed the floors. The bouncer came over and told Deco he had to leave the club. I tried to intervene and said that the beer was mine, not Deco's, and he was just taking a sip because he was thirsty. This backfired. Now I was in line for ejection because I left a minor drink alcohol – sounds gas but that's how it was. He said that once he put out Deco, he would be back for me. As he dealt with his first victim, I scooted outside, hopefully out of sight of my potential captor.

Five minutes later he was back for his prize and came over to me. Despite this he wasn't 100% sure that I was the guy, so he asked me if I had given an underage person some of my beer. Looking at him with a perplexed expression I replied.

'What?' adding even more doubt to his mind.

Then he asked what I had been drinking. By now I'd finished and disposed of my can. I had been drinking Bud, but I told him I was drinking Coors. When I asked what was the matter, he said he must have the wrong person and apologised. At last, I had got the better of one of the bouncers and it felt great. The spanner.

The last of the rebels took an early shower as Renee was dismissed for being unable to walk straight. Or for that matter, walk at all.

As with every week, a huge group of people congregated outside the club at the end to talk. I was talking to Bruce when Nevaeh came over and told us about her bitter encounter. As Bruce's friends were trying to take a picture, she had told a particular girl to 'get out of the way' because she was blocking the view. This didn't go down well. The girl turned around and blasted about how ignorant Nevaeh was and labelled her the biggest bitch in Hyannis. What made this peculiar was that she didn't even know Nevaeh, had never met her in her life. Though hammered, Nevaeh was hurt and upset at the verbal attack. There was only one way I could think of cheering her up. The next thing you know we were off to Christy's for a cream cheese bagel. That would be sure to cure what ailed her.

I decided to skip going to Boston to work on Helga's house for the three days. Apparently it was out in the countryside, which would mean all work and no play in the city, and the workers were supposedly housed in the basement to sleep. No thanks. I had developed a dead rat phobia ever since the Best Value Inn. The weather had cleared up by now and the caddying was thriving. I was getting out on the course most days, which did a lot to help ease my financial concerns.

There were very few days when I'd go on two loops. The heat and the weight of two bags would normally be enough to sap your energy reserves; and left you panting to get home for a cold drink and a chance to put your feet up and check out what sort of unusual situations Tim The Tool Man Taylor was finding himself in.

One day I was handed the job of caddying for a wealthy, older-than-middle-aged man, who was very well known in the club, along with his friend. After a near exhausting round on one of the hottest days, the old fart handed me a measly $55. I stood there in disbelief. It was $5 short of the average most caddies were paid for a double bag. I felt like taking the notes with the pictures of different dead presidents and ramming them so far up his arse that the next time he coughed they came out his feckin' mouth. Livid, I walked off to collect my bag from the caddyshack. One of the young trainee pros came over and asked if I'd like to go for another round. I didn't really want to, I was wrecked, but he said they would pay me well for my assistance. Well, it couldn't be any worse than the last round, so I agreed to caddy for them. I couldn't get the thought out of my head that more money meant more beer.

After four hours we walked off the eighteenth. It hadn't been that bad. They were from the Big Apple and were sound, decent people. That helped the time go quicker. They handed me some rolled up notes and thanked me for my help. When I looked at the money later, I nearly collapsed. They had given me $100. Instantly, I had a hallucination, and I saw different beers flying around my head just waiting to be grabbed. This made up for caddying for the crusty old scabby leech earlier.

The night before we moved out, we answered the call of the Blue Room. Thanks to Michael's connections, we were treated to cocktails for most of the night at a knockdown price. Most of the others were drinking back in the house. Nevaeh was enjoying a couple of large bottles of Steel Reserve, a beer that had an 8% alcoholic volume. It tasted like cats piss but it did the job. A big bottle cost just two dollars – a bargain in anyone's language. She was a good drinker, unlike Clare, who was normally conked out on the chair after a few drinks like Mr T after a plane jab.

On the way home the both of us were half locked but as happy as Pooh in a honeypot. The thought of a party back in the house beckoned us on, full of spirit. As we cycled down Ocean Street Michael started singing *The Irish Rover* in full voice. I looked behind me to see a car attempting to pass him. Michael was pretty much out of it and didn't realise what was happening. He cycled with wild abandon and couldn't keep a straight line. As the car moved out to pass, Michael edged out from the curb. The car continued to move out trying to give Michael a wide berth. I watched this hilarious dual between bike and car, not giving any thought of where I was cycling. Tears of laughter welled from my eyes, and the situation was made all the funnier because Michael was oblivious to what was going on.

He had reached the middle of the road still singing the classic rebel song with vibrant enthusiasm. At this stage the car was touching the ditch on the other side of the road. I guessed he probably knew that the mad fucker in front of him was drunk, and decided to refrain from using the horn in case Michael got a fright and fell under his wheels. Eventually the car slid past the two-wheeled obstacle, and I don't think Michael noticed there was a car even when it overtook him. From then on that song took on a whole new meaning and a smile would come to my face whenever I heard it played.

On our safe arrival back to camp, Nevaeh had drunk the Steel Reserve too dismissively and forfeited the right to stay up any longer. She said her good nights and made the stuttering walk back home to bed.

What an unnecessary expense of time and energy it was moving out for the week. Packing, cleaning, trying to find a place to stay – it was all bollocks, but non-negotiable. Emma, Maria and Laoibhse were to move into the house of the 'ladies of the night' across the road, while Sheila would stay with a friend she knew from back home. Jack and Alyssa stuck together and were being put up in Pat and Caroline's house for the seven nights.

When moving-out day arrived, Michael and I had nowhere to go. Mainly cause we were lazy slobs and didn't bother asking anyone. The Cork lads had moved out of the Travel Inn a few days beforehand into a dirty, spider-infested hole of a basement beside the airport. Living in the motel wasn't economically feasible any longer so they had to find somewhere cheaper for the month. We had a very generous invitation to rough it with them but we declined because the place was already packed. On the day in question we text Mocha and asked if we could stay with him. A few minutes later, it was confirmed. We had somewhere to rest our weary drunken heads for the week.

Around that time bitter neighbours tried to have the twenty-one people, who lived in the house by the lake, slung out. They ratted Sophie, Isabelle, Patrick, Vincent and Co to the police and also made phone calls to health and safety and the local newspapers. Photographs were taken of the supposedly inhumane conditions they lived in (which, I add, none of the Irish were perturbed by as long as they could fall asleep under the loving touch of Jack Daniels and associates), and were plastered on both the front and back pages of the Cape Cod Times. These were accompanied by a totally one-sided article condemning both the people and their behaviour. According to the law, only ten people should have been allowed to inhabit the house.

The reporter went around asking for names. One of the lads declared himself as Roy Keane, which everyone chuckled at, but the scribbling writer was clueless and had no idea of the man's reputation. The begrudging neighbours failed in their quest to have them all thrown out and the twenty-one guys and girls stayed till the final whistle.

A few of the lads who lived on Pleasant Street, notably the two guys that worked in the Travel Inn, were flung out on their ear by their incensed landlord. Having had enough aggravation from parties he decided to give them their marching orders forcing them to find alternative accommodation for the remainder of the summer. They ended up seeking refuge in the motel where five of them shared a room.

Mocha was a funny fucker, worthy of his place on the radio. Without doubt, he was the finest and nicest American we met all summer. Mocha was the closest thing to an Irishman you could find. With a humorous dry wit and a fondness for the banter, he was up there with the rest of us. It was almost as if he was an Irishman trapped in an American's body. Even the kind hospitality he showed us was another reason to believe that he may have been born in Sligo. Tracing his roots back three generations, his family had, like millions of others, come to the States in search of a better life.

As two avid, yet mediocre golfers, during the late afternoons when the course was quiet we would go tooth and nail at each other and play for the honour of our respective lands and for our own pride (he beat me most of the time). Sometimes if we were a bit tired, we'd grab a few beers and practise shots from 150 yards' in with a wedge on the ninth, while Nevada beat around the place till he was on the verge of having a mild coronary.

And Michael was right there with him.

On Michael's day off, and with the caddying prospering (well paying anyway), the pair of us decided to get out of Hyannis and visit Provincetown, otherwise known as P Town. It was the first time all summer we had been outside of Hyannis, apart from the very first night staying in Boston. And where better to go, than to the gay capital of the northeast.

An empty bus (I wonder why), and a couple of hours later, we reached the very tip of Cape Cod. Had we have kept going and the bus was somehow able to fly, the next landmass we would have hit was Ireland. P Town was very different than the rest of the Cape. It felt like you had been transported down to Florida.

With a population of just 3,500 it's not a big place. But during the summer this number balloons to fill every guesthouse and hotel on the ten square-mile of land. It is surrounded by water, with the Atlantic on one side and Cape Cod Bay flanking the other. The first pilgrims to land on American shores landed here. When they left, as they were about 600 miles away from their intended position, fishermen, traders, smugglers, and pirates made this place their regular port of call.

Gambling and drinking for weeks on end gave Provincetown a somewhat wild reputation.

There were two narrow parallel Main Streets that were connected by a series of smaller streets. They were packed with shops – mostly card and fudge shops, with the odd few sex shops dotted here and there. Restaurants of every nature, and clubs and bars made up the rest.

Burly, muscular men strolled the streets hand-in-hand, stopping every now and then for a loving, sensual kiss. They may have been big and strong on the outside but below this superficial exterior was a girl that longed to be taken from behind. It didn't do much for my appetite and suddenly food didn't seem like such a good idea. Not leaving the women out of course. They were butch and tattoo-ridden, with short army-style haircuts and most looked like they were on 'shag-leave'. They were in the same boat as the girly-boys and used the place as their own personal erotic retreat.

We decided to pop into one of the sex shops. It wasn't like home, where they were something of a taboo, hidden beneath the ground in a seedy basement. These were regular middle-of-the-road stores that were open to everyone. The shop was jammed. I hadn't seen this many horny people since the first night in Pufferbellies. There was everything you could imagine, from whips and chains that the fervent men could experiment with, to nipple rings and vibrators for the ugly dykes, as well as a wide selection of porn for the lonely, single person who wasn't having the best of luck attracting a partner. I took down one of the outfits and put it over my clothes for Michael to photograph. One of the staff came over to us.

This guy was as gay as Christmas. No, he was actually gayer than Christmas he was that gay. His voice had completely turned to a squeaky feminine pitch. He/she told us we weren't allowed take pictures in the shop. Michael and myself looked at each other, confused by the bony character's demand. We couldn't fathom why we weren't allowed take a few snaps. But we didn't bother asking why because the expression on his face would have cracked an egg. There was the possibility of being whacked around the place with a handbag so we put the camera away. Maybe if I had offered him Michael for the night his attitude might have changed. Even then we probably wouldn't have got any pictures, as he would have employed the camera as a kinky aid for his sexual exploits.

Scared that we may be propositioned to be the master of the bitch we carried on our adventure in gayland. I stopped at a card shop to buy a card for my brother whose birthday was in a week's time. Opting to steer clear of the explicit 'one-track mind' cards, I sent him a Garfield card describing how I was in his dream world and possible birthplace. To set the record straight my brother is straight, despite having a drawer-full of CDs from artists such as George Michael and Elton John. Everywhere we walked there seemed to be middle-aged men lip-locking with the added bonus of a bit of tongue thrown in.

To escape the potent visual images that bombarded us, we sought shelter in a beach bar. Ordering drinks from a lesbian isn't as much fun as you might think. We were given ice-cold stares as she handed us our lukewarm beers. To be safe, we sat as far away from the bar as possible, which put us nicely into gay men territory who were busy swimming in the pool. There was no escaping the gay community – it was impossible. So we turned our chairs to face the ocean and pretended we were in an all-straight haven surrounded by heterosexual goddesses.

Come the end of the day, we were relieved to be leaving P Town. I'd say we were the first ones on the bus that would take us back to Hyannis. A whole day there was a little too long, and though I was glad of the experience, it's one I won't be rushing out to repeat.

DJ Bollocks

11

The three girls settled tightly into Nevaeh's house. With six people already living there (along, for a time, with a guy from Galway and Clare's boyfriend) the extra bodies were pounding on the pressure on the mere two-bedroomed home. Bags and suitcases littered the sitting room, which became a bedroom through necessity. Despite the squeeze, these situations added to the fun and enjoyment, with a few wild and wacky occurrences thrown in for good measure. Every now and then the English girl living there would bring her fanatically hairy American boyfriend back for a spot of rock and roll loving, just to spice up the atmosphere a tad.

One afternoon, as Emma was enjoying a peaceful siesta, she was rudely awoken by what she could only describe as, 'a gawking crow' (Susie had unwittingly burst into song). Her door suddenly burst open. Opening her eyelids and lifting her head, she saw a ghastly figure appear in the doorway. Emma thought she was having a nightmare. Susie stood there modelling her new thong, which had the added extra of having a hole in them. To make sure Emma's full attention was directed on her new knickers, she wore nothing else but a smile. Emma was scared. She feared for her sexual sanity. Susie wasn't the thinnest girl in the world, although she did make the effort to go to the gym a few days a week. Though, afterwards, in need of a reward for all her efforts, the Ben And Jerry's ice cream pots would normally be cleared out. Emma did eventually recover from the trauma, but it took the assistance of eight vodkas and a couple of shots to help her forget it.

Once we started living with Mocha my energy levels soared. As his house was located just off the ninth fairway I was getting an extra fifteen minutes sleep in the morning. This might not sound like a lot, but when you're getting up at half five with the rabbits, the added few minutes feels like an eternity. All I had to do was grab a bowl of Frosties, then cycle around the outskirts of the course on the paths that led to the clubhouse, instead of making my usual uphill slog to the club. Michael suffered the opposite faith, but at least he didn't have to be in work until eleven every morning, and it was downhill. He could roll all the way ensuring not to put too much strain on his boozed-up lifeless body.

The majority of the time I'd be home by two or three and fall into the gaff, collapse on the couch with heat exhaustion and join Mocha for a bit of TV. He normally took a nap for a couple of hours at around four, as he was up every morning an hour and a half before me. One day I got home early, and he and Alice, his girlfriend, invited me to a barbeque in one of his work colleague's houses. I was chuffed at the chance of having some decent food and happily accepted their invite.

Alice had just bought a beautiful new jeep, and I was treated to a trip in this fancy 4x4 that still had that new car smell wafting around inside. There were about twelve people there and I was introduced to them all. It helped that I was Irish, giving me somewhat of a celebrity status so I was never short of folk to talk to. First and foremost, the most important aspect to me was the food. There was an impressive variety being served by the hosts, including two or three different types of meat, prawns and crab on crackers, salads (I stayed away from them), and other goodies.

By the end of the barbeque I think they regretted bringing me along. They had never seen such a gluttonous Irish guy in full flow, and probably didn't want to see one again. I washed it all down with a few beers, a couple of Cape Codders (vodka and cranberry) and a relaxing game of soccer with Alice and the kids. Despite being merry, I managed to beat off my football rivals. They weren't prepared for my silky Irish skills and were, quite literally, flabbergasted by them. Alice had been invited to a party out in Sandwich, which was about a thirty-minute drive from where we were. After no shortage of arguments between the two quarrelling lovers, we were on the road to her friend's house to collect them for the party.

There was no love lost between Mocha and Alice's friends; he wasn't their favourite guy. There was one in particular, who had a boy's name that was a slang word for a penis. He despised her because she kept trying to persuade Alice to dump him. When we picked both of the friends up, there was a tense atmosphere in the car. The girl, with the manhood nickname, had a forceful, intimidating nature about her, and wasn't backward about coming forward with biting opinions and crude criticisms. I could understand Mocha's trouble in liking her.

As we drove along, the girls decided to throw a couple of beer cans out the window to see if they could hit some old man who was walking along the path. They missed, but Mocha was exasperated by their behaviour. Secretly boiling with having to come to the party, every little incident like this helped to slowly but surely push him over the edge.

When we arrived at the party, held in someone's garage, a few guys were playing pool. It wasn't exactly the most happening party. It was mostly guys who had turned up, worst luck for me. Mocha was uncomfortable; he didn't fit in with this sort of folk. It must be hard when your girlfriend is fourteen years younger than you are, and you're forced to hang around with people you have nothing in common. They were a different generation, and because of this Alice's friends despised and ignored Mocha, giving him the cold shoulder most of the time.

He wanted to go home shortly after getting there. He wasn't enjoying himself and didn't see any reason to be in a place where he wasn't fully welcome. Alice asked him to give it a chance; he just might have a good time. But there was determination in his eyes, and a stout denial that the garage gathering could in any way improve. This wasn't helping relations between the two and seemed to draw out even more resentment between them. The situation was becoming stale so Alice decided to give in and go home. It had been a flying visit, one where I managed to get my paws on a couple of beers, so I was happy out.

A few sips were in order when we arrived back at the house. The three of us proceeded to get langered on beer and bountiful helpings of Absolute Vodka with Red Bull. In need of a game to play we decided to initiate drunken strip poker (score-loads of double cheeseburgers doesn't prepare you well for such a merriment). It was a fierce battle and one that I very quickly lost. Before I knew it I was sitting on the couch totally starkers. In the end Alice came out victorious, but since she was having the pleasure of seeing two fine handsome men without any clothes on (you love yourself more with drink), she thought it only fair to repay the compliment.

Michael was down having a few jars with some friends at the time. Who knows what he would have thought if he had walked in on the three of us sitting there drinking in the buff. Knowing Michael, though, he probably would have stripped off and joined us.

And from then on I made a point of practising my card-playing skills.

Michael and Emma broke up just before we moved out of the house. They decided it would be best to take a break from each other because they just couldn't seem to get along. They had been arguing and fighting and resenting each other for the best part of the summer so far. They thought a bit of time apart might make the heart grow fonder. It was a difficult period for them as it was so public. It was damn near impossible to keep any sort of secrets or hide any hurt or grievances they were suffering with. They had no place where they could be on their own to talk about things, and there were so many people around that they never had any privacy.

Emma was heartbroken at how things were going. It was tough to experience this under the glare of the public eye and not have anywhere she could go for sanctuary. She tried not to grieve in public but at times the emotion of the situation overwhelmed her and she'd burst into tears. We all did our best to reassure her that everything would come good in the end. She just had to be patient. Her eyes were often a pinkie-red colour when she had been crying in her room. It was sad to see someone suffering like this. It wasn't the right environment to be trying to arrange your thoughts and clear your head. The break up had been on the cards for a while, and all their friends could do was just be there for them and hope for the best.

I rose with the birds the next morning in search of riches, well, hopefully 3-score at least. I was to be employed that day by the most in-tune and closest couple I had ever seen. They were a few years short of the big 60. He was about six stone overweight, and because of this they also decided to take a cart. If he walked anymore than about twenty paces, his T-shirt became a lake.

The pair of them clicked and got on like characters from a fairytale. They were best friends and cherished spending time together and taking part in mutual hobbies. The acceptance of everything they were and their closeness was highlighted by their use of endearing nicknames for each other; like how he would compliment any small achievement made on her behalf by referring to her as 'dude'. It was fantastic to see the spark of love and obvious intimacy still burning bright after more than thirty years of marriage. In today's day and age that is an exceptional achievement, and more than likely aided by the fact they were high-school sweethearts. They were what every couple on this earth aspires to be.

They were decent golfers. Even with the presence of a cart the husband's stamina decreased dramatically after a few holes, and found it an uphill task to continue the type of prowess he had demonstrated in the early part of the game. I either ran beside the cart (which did wonders for my fitness), or else I drove it (which undid all the good work of my running), depending on what stage they were at on the hole. I caddied for them three or four mornings. This was great as they booked me in advance, which guaranteed me payment, and ensured I didn't have to hangout in the caddyshack for hours on end. They paid handsomely and the rounds had a tendency to fly by. The three of us would chat about anything that came to mind and there was plenty of lively, witty banter. I described to them how drunk I had been the previous night and how I was still hung over, and in-turn, they let me in on the many cocktails they had last evening, as well as the skinny dip they had taken together that morning in their Jacuzzi; there could only be one winner in this verbal exchange so I zipped it.

He had his own business in New York City, and holiday houses in four different parts of the country. He even offered me, my family, my girlfriend the use of his New York penthouse apartment if I was ever in his neck of the woods. Working for them had made it worth going through the suffering of all the assholes I had caddied for during my short spell as a caddy.

Later on, Michael and I treated ourselves to a night in Pufferbellies for all our hard work. We began things in Mocha's to get us in the mood, and headed off. As I pelted down the road, I glanced behind me. Michael was nowhere in sight. He must be back around the corner. This didn't prove to be such a clever move after the Absolute Vodka (if you ever take this drink, you will notice that it has a rather unpleasant habit of kicking-in unexpectedly a while later) and I lost my balance scanning the road for Michael. The bike collapsed to the right, fortuitously as it happened or I could well have been another truck's road-kill, and I hit the ground with an almighty wallop and tumbled onto a grassy bank. My loyal baby had betrayed me, inflicting cuts and bruises on my battered body. I was glad the drink had gone to my head because that fall could have been very sore. It was nothing a few more beers wouldn't cure. And as my mammy would say, 'you'll be better before you're twice married'.

I got up and dusted myself off – didn't want to go to the club looking like a knacker who had just sold a pony. Wouldn't you know it, as I was hopping back onto Martha (I had forgiven her for the little stunt she had just pulled), Michael bowled along and hit the deck just before he reached me. This unbelievable coincidence had me gasping for air through violent snorts of laughter. I literally peed my bleach-designed jeans, ensuring that I had, in fact, reached knacker status.

Once again, Sunday night lived up to its ever-rising reputation. The only words that could be used to describe it were 'class', or if you hailed from the great city of Boston, 'phat'. Skipping the weekly function in Nantucket Street, we headed back to Mocha's. When you've been on the batter all evening this cycle was a bitch. Uphill most of the way, near total darkness, and alcohol filtering nicely around your system made it a reassuringly tough struggle.

For the fun of it we decided we'd take a short cut through the golf course. We reached the gates of the club, which were locked, but it was possible to scale them without much trouble. On the verge of climbing the gates, a white security jeep drove menacingly up the hill. Jesus, we were up on the bikes in a flash. The security man patrols the Hyannis Port area every night on account of its prosperous inhabitants that included people like the Kennedys and the Shrivers. But I knew of another entrance not too far from our present location.

There was something eerie about a golf course at night, as we cycled daringly across the immaculately tended fairways. We made our way across the whole course, trying not to fall into a water hazard or pot bunker. Without realising it, there was dew on the grass. Our tire tracks could clearly be traced right back to the house just off the ninth. No one seemed to notice our disrespect for the links and we lived to cycle another course.

The following night we decided to stay in and do what we normally did – drink, chat, and listen to some mesmerising dance tunes. It was like an escape from reality. The three of us would sit in the living room, chill out and drift off with the music to different places in our imaginations. After eating our staple diet of pasta, with a bit of pasta and a side of pasta, we'd be suffering from a carb overdose, so we couldn't go anywhere even if we wanted to. It was considered bad luck if we didn't help the pasta reach the stomach with waves of vodka so naturally we had to oblige our superstitious natures.

Mocha had offered to have both of us on his radio show, but every time there was a suitable slot either Michael or I had to work. This night we made a pact that the following morning, or should I say three hours' time, we would get up no matter how bad the hangover and help Mocha host the show. With that we hit the sack – well Michael slept on a few cushions on the floor and I sprawled across the couch. Since Mocha had only one bedroom, they were our beds for the week, and we thanked the founders for giving alcohol the ability to knock us out no matter where we lay our heads.

Holy shit, that was a quick three hours.

The hangovers raged. Our heads looked as if they had been smacked around by Satan's evil minions. But somehow they managed to calm the nerves and kill the butterflies that fluttered like fuck in our bellies (or was that the vodka that hadn't quite yet drained; I wasn't sure).

Mocha hosted the programme with another girl. She was a mother of three, had tattoos plastered all over her body, and was extremely mellow; but a nice person overall. Surprisingly enough it turned out well, with no major blunders or mishaps to ruin our first radio appearance. We were even allowed to say 'bollocks'! Now, how mighty was that. The Americans weren't familiar with that word so we took the opportunity to say it as many times as we could, bollocks. Near the end of the show, a girl getting ready to go work in a pizza restaurant rang in to request a dedication. Mocha asked her if she'd like to talk to the Irish bollocks boys and she was delighted to make our acquaintance. He then asked her if she and a friend would like to go on a double date with the boys from Ireland. This sudden flash of inspiration was an interesting thing to run on the radio, could be a real crowd pleaser. She was happy to go out on a double date with us. We decided to call it, 'The Potato Date'.

Everything on the date would be Irish, from the meal to the pub. It was a chance to show the girls of America what an Irish date would be really like – excluding the vomiting and making a fool of yourself that normally resulted back home. Unfortunately it never came to fruition. *Dismissed* could count its lucky stars and be thankful that it was too late in the summer to start such a programme. It was a pity because as far as voices went they sounded cute. She never did get to ask for her dedication. We guessed it was because she was so excited to have the opportunity to go out with a couple of authentic Irish alcoholics.

Bollocks.

It came as a shock to discover Jack had been made redundant from his job. Two other people had been sacked, including an American who had been working there for a long spell. Contracts were starting to dry up and they couldn't afford to hold on to all their staff, so the unavoidable happened.

The staffing agency managed to hook Jack up with employment with another landscaping firm that was owned and run by a guy from Dublin – it really was a small world. He had lived on the Cape for the last six years, and in the winter he and his girlfriend, who was also from Ireland, would head down to Florida to follow the work and the sun. His business had flourished and had received rave reviews in many of the local papers. His success allowed him his very own army-style Hum V. The seats in the back had been taken out and he had converted the space into a private 'relief area', covered with sheets and cushions to be used when the girlfriend and he were on the road.

Laoibhse, too, took an early bath from her job only to get it back a few days later. Her boss, who was no older than herself (probably even a little younger), took on the responsibility of checking a few guys' IDs when they ordered drinks from Laoibhse. When she had given the all clear, Laoibhse then proceeded to take their order and serve them drinks. Somehow it turned out that they were underage and Laoibhse was blamed and subsequently fired by her thick bitch of a boss.

None of the girls in the Duck got on with their spoiled supervisor, and this was a sign of her total incompetence. However, through some consultation, Laoibhse was reinstated as a waitress and enjoyed a few days' holiday in the process.

Elsewhere, Sophie and Isabelle were doing their utmost to be employed by every institution in Hyannis. After the failed painting gig – their employer didn't pay them and Isabelle spilt a whole bucket of Ralph Loren Saint paint on a bedroom floor (which wouldn't come out) – they then made their way to Bed Bath And Beyond beside the mall. It sold everything to do with houses. Next in line was the Internet Café on Main Street which came in handy for free internet use as it usually cost a scandalous $4 for fifteen minutes Net time – not good if you were involved in a passionate, no-holds-barred cybersex session.

Chillies restaurant chain offered them a job after attending an interview, but they were let go a minute before they were scheduled to start because they weren't looking for seasonal staff – must have been a thoroughly rigorous interview process. Originally they had secured jobs in the Duck, but had to be made redundant before they could start because of the inclement weather and the subsequent lack of business.

Deco had finally been paid what he was owed by the airline company after weeks of work. His creditors could now be paid in full, every last one of them. Every now and then he would fail to turn up for work due to the hazards of Cape Cod nightlife. When this occurred Jacob had to work twice as hard unloading all the fat tourists and their cases from the plane. This was to be expected, though, and I think the company knew this because they never really took him up about his absences.

A couple of the girls sharing the house with Nevaeh and Clare were working in the Melody Tent. This was the venue that staged regular concerts during the summer. Maggie got to work backstage as acting personal assistant to the Stars. It was her responsibility to service the big names (in a non-sexual context of course) and meet their every whim and want. She looked after the needs of people like Tom Jones, Lisa Marie Presley, Hootie And The Blowfish, the Beach Boys and many more. When Mr Jones first started talking to her she suffered from an acute case of celebrity nerves and clammed-up. Not knowing whether to take her knickers off and throw them at him or just offer herself on the entrée table, she ended up just spluttering jumbled words in his direction. He must have been just as good-looking in person as he was on TV.

As time went by she became more acquainted with some of the finest musicians in the world, and the job became second nature to her. She felt like she was born to handle the affairs of the rich and famous; she also managed to regain her voice and composure the next time she bumped into Tom Jones.

He now gives her knickers pride of place on his bedroom wall at home.

Jessica wasn't having things so easy in Gringo's restaurant. Her boss was a bit of a heartless swine and both of them were often at loggerheads. They didn't see eye to eye at all and arguments sparked-off on a regular basis. She would sometimes be hurt and upset by some of the cruel things he said to her, but she managed to get some reprieve by dictating her hours and only working the shifts she wanted.

The tradition of peace between the Irish was under severe threat one night outside Kendrick's nightclub. A great night had by all, Michael and I were saying our goodbyes, as we had to be up early for work the next day. Walking down the road towards our bikes and hidden cans, a couple of the guys from Nantucket Street began throwing insults our way. We let fly with a few peaches of our own and wanted to leave it at that. Then they began daring us to go across to them. Another guy had just joined them and they were calling us every name under the sun. Michael was quite intent in going over and putting a stop to the constant barrage of taunts that were coming from their loud mouths but I saw no point in it. I didn't like fighting for stupid reasons and quite frankly they weren't worth the effort.

Out of nowhere five guards arrived on the scene, putting a stop to any thoughts of a fight.

Kendrick's again was to be the centre of controversy the following week, when Deco and John ran into two black lads and a white girl on their way home to the motel. They all got chatting and the boys invited them in for a drink. Topics ranging from the forty shades of green to the fondness the Irish have for the ale were discussed between the newly integrated black and white scene.

The visitors offered to sell Deco some quality hash, which he happily accepted. The only snag was they didn't actually have it on them and said they would have to go to their brother's house down the road to collect it. They then asked Deco for the thirty dollars. He refused, saying he'd give them the money on receipt of the goods. The guy Deco was talking to insisted his other two mates would stay while he shimmied off to pick up the drugs.

Reluctantly, he handed over the notes, comforted by the fact that they had built up a good rapport with them. Walking out the back door, the drug baron hopped up onto the path, and was away down the road. The other two imitated their friend's manoeuvre and hurried off after him. A feeling of helplessness swept over Deco, and he and John sprinted after the untrustworthy trio. Once they had caught up, Deco said he didn't want the weed and demanded his money back. After a further couple of futile attempts to convince the guys to part with his money, one of them turned around and planted Deco, sending him crashing to the ground. Not wanting to leave John out, they swung at him, too, laying him out beside his friend on the cold concrete.

Furious, the boys ran back to their room and grabbed the hurls they had brought over with them. They never did find the con men who had managed to swindle thirty quid from them. It was a lesson learned the hard way plus a couple of shiners they would sport for several days.

The last of the seven nights had come and it ended on a spectacular note. Blanket lightning and thunder lit the night sky. Every couple of seconds bolts of spear-like lightning flashed angrily across the dark sky. The thunder rumbled all night. It was a sight to behold; I had never seen anything like it before. It was like Mother Nature was staging a show demonstrating to all her intense power.

With a few jars taken I was feeling brave. I walked outside, stood in the garden and raised my arms to the heavens imagining that I was controlling this incredible phenomenon. I escaped being fried while I was living out my fantasy, and I called it a day when the rain started to pour down on top of me. This, too, was hair-raising, flooding Cape Cod completely, forcing me to abandon the idea of working the next morning. I was devastated.

What a ride!

12

Home at last. The nine usual suspects had been reunited. We would only have the pleasure of staying in this magnificent pad for another couple of weeks.

It was possible to notice the place slowly starting to empty even at this relatively early stage. Deco was flying home in a couple of days, as he had to repeat the two exams he had failed. He had originally planned to stay on and not bother going back, opting instead to have another crack at the year. It was a last minute change of mind that saw him leave, regrettably. His departure was to leave him emotionally scarred for life, as that particular day would turn out to be one of the worst days of his twenty years on this planet.

When he woke up that morning, he discovered his passport was missing. Deco had brought it to Kendrick's the previous night and had somehow mislaid it. He phoned Usit immediately. They told him that he would have to have his birth cert sent to the Consulate Building in Boston, and that he was to go there himself to collect his emergency passport – which would cost $20.

The sprint was on. Deco's flight was at 1.30pm so he had to be quick. With no time for goodbyes, Deco reached the airport. He asked if it would be possible to leave his bags there. His request was flatly refused. With that he legged it out in search of a taxi to the Consulate.

'Shite! No taxi.'

Out of nowhere came a shout.

'If you want I can give you a lift and it's the same price as a taxi.'

With no time for deliberations, he grabbed his opportunity and jumped into the black stretch limo. Unfortunately (and as Deco himself puts it, 'and retard here believed him') this wasn't the case. A credit card and $30 was all Deco had in the world. The limo came to $39. Then he made another paralysing, heart-stopping discovery – his credit card was gone. He desperately explained his situation to the limo driver who took pity on him and accepted the $29 Deco offered, as he needed to keep a dollar for the T.

As the lift approached the fourth floor, Deco was positively shaking, as if he had been left tied to a lamppost in P Town after a stag night. He now had to try and wangle a passport with no money to pay for it. The employee stared at Deco in amazement as he told how he had lost both his passport and credit card in one fowl blow of faith's cruel hand. They agreed to pay for his passport on the condition he send them the $20 in the post. With these two formidable obstacles overcome, he still had the onus of getting to the airport on time and catching the right train to bring him there.

Deco was to get a helping hand when one of the staff said he'd give him a lift to the airport as he was collecting someone there anyway. He arrived on time, and was told he'd have no trouble travelling from Boston to Philadelphia, but may have to upgrade his ticket to first class from there to Shannon.

This would cost a total of $100.

Deco currently had a total of $1.

Another good break was to befall Deco as he found a call card with some credit still remaining. He rang his Mam and quickly got her credit card number. On the way to Philly, Deco's mind was besieged by worry. He knew that if he didn't succeed in getting a seat on the next plane, he'd have to start sparring with dead cows in an attempt to fight the heavyweight champion to make a few dollars to pay for his long awaited trip home.

After some difficulties with his Mam's credit card number at the counter in Philly, it was finally accepted. But Deco was told he might not be able to board as he wasn't suitably dressed for first class. It was a five-hour wait for his flight back to Shannon, made all the longer by stress and an empty stomach since he had no money to buy food. When the time came, he was made wait till the end of the queue. These were the scariest few minutes of the day, a day where everything seemed to be working against him. He didn't fancy having to run the steps of the Philly Art Museum every morning after guzzling down three raw eggs from a tall glass. With everyone on board, he waited alone with baited breath.

'You may get on sir, there is a spare seat, but it's in the economy section.'

Not sitting in first class had never sounded so good and he didn't give a fiddlers fuck that he had just wasted $100 as he lunged for the empty seat before anyone else had a chance to take it.

Roy and Al had left, too. They had even extended their stay, switching their original departure dates. But money shortage forced their hand. There was a part of them that wanted to miss their flight and even swim home later so they could stay until we were all leaving.

No one had any desire to swap this place for the old boring routine at home. This was freedom, pure and simple. Going home would be like being trapped in a cage unable to wriggle out. Restrictions and responsibilities would constrict any freedom you'd crave and you'd lose the new friendships that had been forged.

People were becoming familiar with, and adapting to, this way of life. They were reluctant to go back to old ways. You had built a life for yourself for three months, worked to survive and strived to create lasting relationships. Even though the majority of the people were flat broke and wouldn't have been able to afford luxuries such as ketchup with their chips, they didn't care. It proved that money came second to things like friends and enjoying this unique slice of life. Once you had money for drink and the odd meal here and there, life was great. And if you were short, no one would leave you out in the cold – if there were two drinks left you would be given one and your guardian angel would have the other.

Suddenly this was wrenched from your grasp and you had no control or say in the matter. If someone had possessed a time stopper machine, chances are we would all still be over there partying up a storm. The dream had to end sometime and the trip back to reality was compulsory. But it didn't deter us from hoping and praying for the invention of that time freezer.

After much soul-searching and finance-evaluation, we came to the conclusion that a road trip would be the perfect idea for our travel plans. Most people had aspirations of exploring America for a week or two at the start of September. After a hectic summer, full of wicked nights and hard work, a holiday was needed to relax the body and sooth the mind. Everyone had different ideas about where to go and what to do paving the way for many diverse and wonderful adventures. September lurked just round the corner and the ball needed to start rolling on organising our perfect getaway.

Michael and I called into the rent-a-car company behind the transportation centre. It was the only company we could find that rented to under twenty-five year olds; albeit at an extra $8 a day for the crime of being only twenty-one. With *National Lampoon's Summer Vacation* in mind, we knew we had to experience this type of a holiday in a station wagon, otherwise it wouldn't have been an authentic road trip.

We ran into the Northern Ireland gang who had hired a car for the day to drive to Six Flags Amusement Park. The manager of the firm was a complete tool, and the Irish who had had contact with him were all of the same opinion: wanker. After five minutes of listening to his lectures and attempted witty remarks, I had to hold Michael back from leaping over the counter and putting his head through the partition. He was one of those guys who was totally arrogant and who brought the meaning of self-love to a new level. So in order to keep our tempers under wraps, we switched off and pretended we were somewhere else, drowning out his eternally annoying ranting.

When all the paper work and words of advice from the muppet behind the counter were dispensed with, we became proud renters of an ugly-looking car for two weeks (which we later changed to one week due to lack of funds). We would hit the road on the first and return to Hyannis on the eighth of September. Nevaeh, Michael and myself were all certs for three out of the five or six available places in the car. Nevaeh and myself ended up changing the date of our flights on two different occasions, setting us back $125. Eventually we decided that we'd fly home on the ninth, the day after coming back from the trip. To help spread the burden of the cost of the car we intended to find another couple of people who would be interested in travelling with us. The search was on.

To make up for the loss of the recently departed regulars, our numbers were rejuvenated with the arrival of friends from home. Sheila's boyfriend, Harry, arrived, accompanied by three of Maria's friends, and Sebastian, a friend of ours from school (and also high up on the pecking order in the army). Emma's older sister, Anna, also made the trip. These people helped add another dimension to the atmosphere and it was great because we all meshed together nicely. With the newcomers, we were now fifteen who ate, slept, and lived in a house that was only meant to accommodate five. We were fortunate that the landlady lived in the city, and she didn't employ the nurse to act as a spy to report our shady dealings back to her. The virgins of the Cape were staying for two weeks, leaving a day after our trip began, which was a pity as it ruled them out of the running for a space in the travelling wagon.

Harry had no idea about Sheila's cavorting antics three thousand miles away. Roy and her had been getting quite close for some time now, and she was planning on telling Harry the story when he arrived. I thought, along with a few others, that this wasn't the time or place to tell Harry about her summer flings. It might ruin his holiday altogether and make him yearn to flee back home. Perhaps it was a prosperous coincidence that Roy had flown home just a day previous. Harry had an easy-going and lovable nature. A giant, he stood at about six foot seven, forcing him to duck beneath every doorframe he encountered.

Happily, despite a slow and bumpy start to their summer relationship, they soon became closer than ever and shared many satisfying times together.

As the rain lashed against the earth we had a wee problem. It was Blue Room night but we'd be sure to be wringing wet if we ventured out to the club. Nevaeh and I were the only two stupid enough daredevils to run the dripping gauntlet. Had we have put on every jacket in Hyannis the rain would still have pierced our protection. After a couple of shots to keep us in working order and a session of psyching each other up, we were away.

When we arrived at the Blue Room we created puddles that had to be mopped up. Word had got round that there was a party in Pleasant Street, so once the night had ended we decided to go gate-crashing.

If our clothes had dried off in the heat of the Blue Room, it didn't last long. After swinging by Christy's to get a couple of bagels, we got to Pleasant Street even wetter than before. We met Sarah, Renee's friend in Christy's, and I had now given both of them a lift on old Martha. She was convinced that she wouldn't be able to have kids after the ordeal and vowed never to get up on my brick of a saddle again.

The house was full and lively, with the bedroom being the busiest hang-out spot. We sat on the bed contentedly eating our late night snacks, despite being somewhat drenched. Nevaeh needed an after-bagel cigarette: with apologies to the inhabitants of the house, we borrowed a full packet from the kitchen (in case you were wondering where they got to).

There was a guy playing 'pin the tail on the donkey' on the kitchen door, blindfolded. I didn't see the need for a blindfold – he was so wasted that he probably wouldn't have been able to locate the donkey's arse anyway. As he was just about to stick the tail inappropriately miles from the animal's backside, the door slammed open banging his arm. Keeping his temper in check, he regained his composure and attempted once again to pin the tail. Funnily, the same thing happened, the door flew open smashing into his arm for the second time. Unable to forgive this infliction, the drunken game player yelled at the top of his voice with the blindfold still securely fastened over his eyes.

'Would ya ever fuck off!'

Nevaeh and I stood rooted to the spot, concerned for Mr Donkey's near future. As he removed the mask from his eyes, there, standing in front of him with the expression of a raging bull, was a cop. Unable to control ourselves we let out some unrestrained back-throat sniggers. Whipping his head round and fixing his angry gaze in our direction he demanded to know what I found so funny. I quietly said that it was very funny, but then retracted my statement in fear of being shot in the groin, and said I saw nothing funny about it at all.

The landlord had rung for the police to come and break up this illegal gathering of people with similar interests. So the police gave us one minute to leave the house, or face arrest. Taking our cigarettes with us, we headed back into the rain soaked night, relieved that we wouldn't be spending the next few hours in a cell with a big black dude named Bubba who had a liking for tight, white asses.

Clare and Sheila joined the 'Betrayed By Your Bike' society, when both suffered nasty accidents. Sheila's handlebars suddenly gave way one evening cycling down Ocean Street, sending her in a penetrating line through the air like the guy in the circus who gets fired out of the cannon. Cuts and slits riddled her entire body, but luckily nothing was broken apart from her pride, which would heal quickly enough.

Clare's accident was potentially fatal, but incredibly got away with only a hurt wrist and mild shock. As she and Nevaeh cruised down the main road one afternoon, Clare, with the imminent ending of the path, jumped the curb and onto the road. Not noticing what was coming, she was hit by a car that catapulted her from her bike and sent her somersaulting through the air. She landed on the bonnet of the car and then rolled off onto the ground. Nevaeh looked on in horror, fearing the worst for her best friend.

A paramedic was in the area and came racing over to help the victim that lay still on the stone. Within minutes there were four more paramedics on the scene examining Clare. Seeing that her friend was alive, Nevaeh was tickled that the original paramedic had big arms. Salivating at the lips, she spent most of the time drifting in and out of her daydream to check her friend was still breathing.

On the topic of life, a tragic accident took place in the early evening one particular day. I was in the middle of giving Mocha a serious trouncing out on the golf course (if ya believe that you believe the Tooth Fairy goes to raves with the Easter Bunny every Monday) when suddenly there came a loud, booming thud. I looked at Mocha and we shifted our gaze skywards to check for thunder and lightning. There was only a blue blanket lightly dotted with lonely puffy clouds.

The next day, we found out that the noise we had heard was in fact the crash-landing of a plane not too far from where we were. The plane was from the airport in Hyannis and it was en route to Nantucket when it went down. The pilots on board were killed instantly but, thankfully, no one else was on the plane. The scary part was that both Deco and Jacob often made that very same journey and with those very same pilots. But they weren't on duty that day. A memorial service was held on the beach for the deceased and as a token of respect the two boys put on some good clothes and headed over to the sands to say goodbye.

At least they would have done had they have gone to the right beach, but they made the effort and they paid their respects in their own individual ways.

In Cape Cod, the Six Flags Amusement Park was advertised everywhere from posters hung on shop windows to TV commercials. It was situated on the other side of Boston, in Springfield, about three hours' drive. One of the employees in Gringo's hired a bus for sixty people in July to take them to the park. Jessica, Clodagh, Renee, and most of Pleasant Street, took the chance to visit this heavily promoted fair. Reports and opinions were extremely positive, and it was the one place just about everyone wanted to go (apart from the lap dancing club outside Hyannis).

It was too good to miss so I set out to organise a bus for the day and try and find some discounts for entry into Six Flags. Unlike the Gringo's bus, we decided to hire a bus for twenty-five, because the headache you'd have trying to firstly find sixty people to go and then trying to get the money from them, could be excruciating. It would be more a friendly affair – enough people to guarantee a mighty day while also ensuring that it was the perfect amount to enable the whole gang to interact. The bus was booked and we were ready to hit the fun park two days later.

For an added bonus it was Laoibhse's twenty-first birthday and we agreed to throw a big party for her when we came back that evening making sure to prolong the agonising ecstasy.

For most of the time we were in America we hung around, on and off, with an American girl that some of the boys from Cork had known the previous year. She didn't live on the Cape, but took regular trips out to visit us for days on end with a different friend every time. She was obsessed with Bono and was head over heels in love with the guy – much to Maria's displeasure. Erin never let the fact that Bono had a girlfriend sway her from attempting to capture the man of her dreams. She never hid her feelings and felt no remorse in conveying her extreme fondness for him, even in the presence of Maria and the rest of us. In Erin's opinion, Bono should rightfully have been hers, and made no effort to repress this feeling. She had a habit of baking a tray-load of cookies for him every time she came over, which was a bad idea, because once Nevaeh and I got a hint of the sweet aroma of freshly-made cookies, all that was left were crumbs (and even then Nevaeh would lick the plate clean).

She wasn't the only one with an infatuation for a 'spoken for' Irish buachaill. The last friend she brought to visit had a severe case of the hots for Michael, and she, also, showed no respect for the fact he had a girlfriend. Like her best friend, she made a move on him one night, only to be emphatically turned-down and reminded of the fact that he was in a relationship of nearly three years.

The two girls lived in hope that the objects of their affection might have a change of heart (or possibly an error in judgement). Despite their not so honourable intentions both guys stood their ground and remained totally loyal to their respective partners, much to the Americans' annoyance. Fair fucks to Bono. I don't think I would have been so strong had someone tried to entice me to the dark side with delicious big chocolate treats.

Sunday night, the best night of the week, and the greatest nightclub in the world (except for The Vibe in Kells) was howling out to us, ready to show us what it was made of. We had been doing nothing but singing its praises to the newcomers, we held it in such high regard. Pufferbellies had to prove itself for the last time to make sure we didn't look like idiots.

To get the most out of our second last Sunday night, we started drinking from about seven, allowing us to go to Pufferbellies early and boogie the night away. To be honest, drink wasn't necessary (not trying to speak ill of the devil's poison), you were on such a high to begin with. It felt like you had been drinking Red Bull all day. Everyone was on a natural buzz, the adrenaline acted as a stimulant providing heaps of energy and lessening inhibitions. Things were so exciting and new that all summer people were happy and bad moods were few and far between. There was something about the place that helped to put you in a great mood, drowning out any possible dark days.

It was the people who made it all worthwhile. Most of the lads over there were bang on. They were looking for fun, able and willing to make anyone a friend. They were open and ready to experience life to the fullest. People were shown in their truest of colours, and the fact where you came from didn't alter attitudes or opinions, made it possible for people to connect on a very deep level. On the Cape you were Irish: not a Dub; or a Corkonian; or a Galweigan;

An equal.

Standing in line, waiting to enter the social haven and place we cherished so much, a bunch of the girls arrived in the back of some guy's jeep. As we are all painfully aware at this stage, walking in heels is a torturous, foot-slaughtering affair, and not one to be taken lightly. Somehow Nevaeh managed to thumb down a jeep and convince the driver to give them a lift to the club. He even took a detour to the local ATM so Nevaeh could get some dollars for the night. Things wouldn't end well for Nevaeh, though. As they were climbing out of the jeep, one of the girls – with her skewer-like heel – stood on her foot causing nerve-slitting pain and a big bruise that would remain with her for some time.

Despite being put up on such a lofty pedestal, Pufferbellies didn't fail to impress every single one of the first timers, and they subsequently fell in love with the place as so many had done before. Lorie, who was a child of music, seemed to teleport into a different dimension, falling into a trance hypnotised by the melodious rhythms. She had come over with her sister Jane and had instantly developed a frighteningly close connection with the club. She couldn't get enough and practically had to be escorted out when the hour of one arrived. We danced the night away and probably a combined weight loss of four stone.

Since we had visitors we decided to bring them to Nantucket Street, to the after-party we disliked so much, the place where we were most unwelcome. We had no trouble getting in and once inside there were no problems at all. It was funny; the girlfriends from home had come over to visit the guys and thus prevented fights from breaking out!

As I was sitting peacefully on the couch, Julie came over and sat on the arm, while Sebastian and Michael occupied the side chair. While I was talking to Julie she was trying to convince me to hook up with her when we got home. She was being very affectionate, planting the odd peck on my cheek, which seemed a bit unusual, as I wasn't reciprocating these expressions at all. It turned out that Michael and Sebastian had been rubbing her back and caressing her arse, and all the time she thought it was me. I could have killed the buggers. I wondered why she didn't leave every time she threatened to.

Outside I came across Renee, who was waiting patiently for a taxi to take her home. We talked until the taxi man arrived, and she cheekily stole a kiss before running over to her lift. It was short but sweet, and she did it without the constant harassment of her friends. This took balls and she earned my respect for her show of bravery and also managed to glue a smile on my face for the rest of the night.

The big day had arrived. We were to meet the bus outside the transportation centre at 6am. It was an early start but many people were used to getting up at that time. It was all going to plan; everyone was out of bed and ready for action. On the way to the bus station there was the almost compulsory stop in Christy's for a breakfast bagel, a bag of Cheetos and a bottle of Gatorade. Most of us were there on time, apart from a couple of the girls who lived with Nevaeh who thought it would be nice to engage in a nice leisurely stroll, while the rest of us waited by the bus thinking of the killer roller coasters we'd soon be on.

Three hours later we arrived in Springfield. After stopping along the way for some mid-morning goodies (slices of pizza), and the viewing of *The Patriot*, which helped elicit braveness in us and spurred us on making us immune to the fear of any white-knuckle rides. Like Mel Gibson, we were ready to face anything that lay in our path with courage and conviction.

We somehow took a wrong turn and ended up at the back of the park, which we thought was the front. Thinking we were the first people there, we soon realised that we were in the wrong place and had to bale back onto the bus. We were soon at the correct gate eager to buy the tickets. In no time we were applying factor 50 and wondering where to go first.

In Six Flags you can hire an electronic device that communicates to you when it's time for you to go on a particular ride. It's quite expensive, but in the long run saved you time waiting in a queue for ages, sweating your bollocks off to get on a ride that would last a total of thirty seconds. A few of us went to get one of these state of the art contraptions at the start of the park, but there was an anaconda-size row of frenetic fun-finders and pages of paperwork to be filled in order to get one.

Stupidly, we decided to forget about hiring one, which, as we found out during the course of the day, would have saved us a lot time standing in long lines being beaten to death by the scalding sun. Two or three of the girls got one, and they flew ahead of the impatient masses, even for the biggest and most popular attractions. We were all nastily bitter watching people sauntering up to the head of the queue as we stood lingering, lost in the crowd.

Most of us split into groups of three or four. This enabled people to cruise the rides together, so they had someone to grab onto when they were reaching torpedo-speed. Michael, Jackie (the dual-named girl who was Michael's co-worker in the Ocean Grill) and I took on the park shoulder to shoulder. Halfway through the day, we ran into the bus driver in the restaurant.

Heather was cool. She was a burly sort of woman, with an eccentric, rebellious streak. She had a husband and three kids at home. I'd say she was a Mam cut from a different cloth but one who her children could look up to and admire. We later found out that she actually owned the bus company, as well as being one of the best drivers I had ever travelled with. Not wanting to leave her on her own, we invited her along with us on our thrill-seeking adventure. She happily accepted.

The biggest roller coaster in the park was aptly named 'The Superman' and was voted the best coaster in the world for the past three consecutive years. The toilet claimed a lot of victims before and after that particular super-hero, but it was well worth the five minutes spent squatting on the bog.

In the afternoon we had planned to chill out in the water park, but opted out when we saw the state of the place. It was chaotic. We felt like chickens in one of those coups. It certainly wasn't the place to be if you were claustrophobic or disliked rubbing off wet, half naked bodies. Michael and I, though, were in no rush to leave. There were some amazing looking water slides, including one that resembled a huge jacks bowl that whipped you around in circles and eventually flushed you out into a pool at the bottom. The queues for these slides were as big as the slippery slopes themselves, and we didn't have enough time to make it worth our while changing into our speedos. Instead we tried to make the most of the time we had left by going on every attraction we could.

It would have been a sin not to hit the bumper cars while we were there. Unlike at home, the ultra-safety conscious Americans would only allow the cars to travel in one direction; even going so far as implementing a curb that ran along the centre portion of the floor which encouraged one-way traffic.

Being your typical not-so-cautious, rule-bending Irish, I swung my car around when I knew Michael and Jackie were behind me and caused a memorable head-on collision with the two lads. The guy who was controlling the cars nearly had a freak attack and used the microphone to fiercely chastise me for my illegal and dangerous actions. But, oh was it worth it (anyway, what's the point of bumpers if you can't cause a couple of bloody noses).

When six o'clock came it was time to hit the road. A great first half of the day had been had and we still had the second part to go – the party – which promised to be a most joyous occasion. Despite the law prohibiting the bus to stop at a liquor store to pick up some booze, Heather made an exception. Half the bus piled into the shop to stockpile their alcohol collection for the long night ahead, and when Michael had finally bought all he needed to buy, we were off to destination 'Tempestuousville'. We all threw a couple of dollars into a bottle for our terrific bus driver who was surprised and flattered by the gesture. It would have been unfair had we not tipped the soundest driver of all time.

I had sort of arranged to meet a girl that I liked at the party, and had been looking forward to it all day. Chloe was from Cork and worked in the Duck with the rest of the girls. She was a bit frustrated at the amount of hours she was lumbered with over the summer. She would have liked more time off to spend with her friends, but nevertheless she became close to the girls, and did manage to fit in a healthy bronze tan along the way.

She celebrated her birthday in July. Her housemates threw a surprise party, and then later that day her new friends threw her a bash in the Duck – not bad for a day's work. Chloe was staying up near the golf course with nine other girls, not to mention the landlord and his five kids who lived directly above them. Preliminary negotiations were carried out about forming their own American Football team, but collapsed due to the absence of a starting quarterback. I didn't get to talk to her for long (long enough, though, to embarrass myself when I forgot what course she was doing in college after being told twice) but she told me to keep in contact when we got home. This I intended to do and I managed to get her number from Laoibhse. I hadn't realised until late on in the summer that I fancied her, but by that time it was too late.

The night had been all we could have wished for. Every thirsty patron had a ball in Ocean Street's most desirable institution (oh, come on! I have to say that). The house had never been so full all the while we were there. People were scattered everywhere from the front garden to the deck out the back to literally hanging out of windows. The arrival of dawn summoned the ending of the birthday celebrations and when the birds began singing, we began snoring.

August so far had been a month of entertainment and excitement, and it wasn't about to let up any time soon. Michael and I had ambitions to visit Nantucket, the island off the coast about an hour away by boat. Vincent had offered us a few free tickets through his ferry connections, but despite our best intentions, we figured it would be better to keep whatever money we had for the road trip. A night out in Boston was also put on the shelf – a new club had recently opened that was modelled on the one in the movie, *Coyote Ugly*, which probably would have been quite a trouser popping experience.

13 Inspector Plod

Emma and Michael had decided to get back together when separation became too tough. This summer had proved to be a considerable spanner in the works of their relationship, and things remained tense and awkward when they reunited. From the beginning till the end things were rough. Another couple might have been driven to such lengths as cheating or just giving up the partnership for good. The three months had driven a stake right through the heart of everything that they had built over the past few years, and threatened any hopes they had for a future together.

Adding to that pressure, Emma wasn't coming with us on the trip. She was staying on to work and save money for the holiday she and Michael were going to take in Boston and New York for a week. Yet, that might also do them a power of good to be totally apart for seven days, hopefully making them reach out for each other like never before.

Mocha and Alice, too, were heading for disaster. Argument after argument was quickly tearing them apart, creating an abyss of bitterness between them. Continuously hanging up the phone on each other, and slagging matches where obscene and brutal insults were regurgitated, their level of trust now bordered on extinct. I had to leave the house one night, deserting my vodka halfway through (no I lie, I knocked it back before I left), as they roared and screamed at each other in his bedroom. It wasn't right for me to be there, they needed privacy – even the dog scampered off out of sheer fright. They spent a lot of the summer apart because whenever they got together a vicious row was more than likely to erupt.

While out and about on his travels, Michael happened to meet Heather, our famed bus driver. She asked him if he'd like to valet park for her but he didn't have a driving licence. But told her I had. I rang her later that day and she offered me the job of acting valet at a wedding that was being held at the entrance to the Cape. Apparently, the hosts were filthy rich and their guests would have bucks dripping from their pockets. More importantly than the money, however, was the opportunity to drive suave, expensive cars and pretend I was a rich and famous celebrity who was going out with Britney Spears. I fantasised about becoming some wealthy, hot-looking woman's toy boy in charge of satisfying her every wish, with the added extra of driving her wherever she wanted to go in her Ferrari.

I accepted the job.

Michael invited Sebastian for a knees-up in the Blue Room, as gratitude for his very considerate gesture when he brought six or seven roomies out to the pub, and paid the entire bill that came close to $300. Sebastian came loaded with money and was prepared to spend it anyway he liked. Michael would be able to get free cocktails for most of the evening and the two boys intended to exploit that to the fullest.

As they laughed and drank out in the comfortable, soft night, three girls of approximately thirty years, who were sitting at the table beside them, began chatting them up. Without hesitation they invited the ladies over, and in return they bought each of the boys a drink. By the end of the night the two lads were ossified, and went to fetch their respective bikes. Appalled by the guys' plans the bouncer, who knew Michael well, refused to let them cycle home in the state they were in and called a taxi instead.

The next morning Michael was in work before his allotted time. The manager and staff looked curiously at him, startled, that he had turned up for work. Convinced that he would be absent judging by his appearance the previous night, here he was bright as a button, ready for work. Michael helped to confirm their opinions of the Irish – that they were a race of incomprehensible, out-of-their-heads alcoholics. In saying that he was on a different planet for most of the day – bringing people soup when they ordered water and prawns when they ordered the bill. Nevertheless, he had turned up on time, and he was working damn hard to ensure the prawns were served before the customers left the restaurant.

I had been told of an infamous drink called 'The Scorpion Bowl', that was served in a Chinese restaurant across the road from the mall. It was a cocktail, and rumour had it, the staff was only allowed serve two per person on account of its deadly potency.

Curiosity got the better of Michael and I and we had to see if the legend was true. To put it simply, it was. They served this explosive beverage in a large cocktail glass with a straw, umbrella and all the 'seaside resort' trimmings. To accompany our liquid dinner we had a plate of chicken fried rice each to help soak up the whore of a drink we were gargling. After just one drink, even with the assistance of the rice, I could see the reason behind their policy of only serving two Scorpion Bowls a piece. Without the money for a second of these monstrosities (thank Christ, cause it would have been a lengthy crawl home), we woozily hopped onto our bikes and attempted to cycle home.

The next day saw me embark on my first adventure as a valet. In order to try and squeeze every last cent out of the twenty-four hours I went caddying that morning. I made $60 for my troubles and even managed to sneak in an hour's worth of TV before Heather picked me up. To my sheer delight, waiting outside in the driveway was a two-seater convertible sports Mercedes. Sebastian and Jack stood there in envious disbelief when they saw my ride; now this was my idea of living the high life.

On the way back to base, she showed me what her baby could do. In a matter of seconds she had the car smoothly racing down the highway at 110mph, the Merc purring under her gentle touch. Even if I was jacked-up on a mixture of cocaine and baked beans and launched down a ninety-degree hill, Martha would still have been left for dead. After a brief stop back in the garage to pick up the other car-parkers, we were heading for someone's special day.

The guests were expected at four. We were told that between the hours of four and five our butts would be worked to the bone. Then our butts could take a long nap, pretty much until eleven that night, when, for another hour, our butts would be back in the hot seat. The house was a hideous, inside out wooden shoebox, but overlooked the ocean atop a cliff. The scenery was nothing short of stupendous, and the car park they were using was down the hill on the water's edge. I just hoped I wouldn't mistakenly drive a Porsche into the sea as I admired the beauty in front of me. When the time came, we were rushed off our feet for the duration of the hour; trying to get all the cars parked as quickly as possible before the people became impatient and denied us our dollar tip.

I felt, as I drove some of the slickest cars on the market, like Michael at a party with a free bar, or Nevaeh with a huge sackful of bagels and cream cheese, or Deco in a sex shop with enough money to cause some serious damage. When all the guests had arrived, the only thing I was looking forward to was the ending of Michael Jackson's *Billie Jean*, and the chance to drive their cars back up to them.

Lounging on the grassy verge in the hot afternoon sun outside the house, we all got to know each other. A police officer had been assigned to handle the traffic situation on the road, to avoid any possible trouble or chaos when all the guests gushed out that evening.

This particular cop resembled someone from a seventies TV show or maybe a cartoon figure such as Postman Pat. He was like a caricature come to life as he sported his hip thirty-year old *Knight Rider* shades. Festively plump and jolly, he was a world away from your typical strict, law-enforcing, rule-following American cop. A rare creature, he told us stories of his many, out of the ordinary, encounters with dangerous and (mostly) stupid outlaws.

Until he told me, I hadn't grasped the significance of his presence at this function. This was a wedding after all, and everyone was going to be half split when they came out at the end of the night. He told us that normally he just hides in a corner and closes his eyes, preferring not to see people collapse legless into their cars. Hats off, he was fuckin' brilliant – now I knew why the organisers had hired him.

We spent almost six hours lazing around with nothing to do. I thought they might have invited us in for a drink or even given us a few stools to sit on as we waited patiently for the guests to totter out. But no, again, we were just the hired servants who weren't entitled to any benefits in kind.

Once darkness started to fall the midgets started to bite. Inspector Plod had some bug spray in his car which we plastered our exposed skin with. When nine o'clock came round, hunger was massacring our bellies, and Plod had been moaning for a feed for some time now. Eventually they brought us into the garage where the food (or should I say leftovers) were being kept and invited us to chow down. Inspector Plod was beside himself with joy – he must have taken four platefuls of grub, devouring the unsuspecting fodder with gentle ease. The food was magnificent and we each grabbed what we could to fill the caverns that had formed in our tummies. This ran conveniently to the end of the night and it was back to work for the guts of an hour.

Some of the cars were stationed right at the edge, with a drop of five feet to the drink. I had to be careful with the automatic systems that operated in most cars. I didn't fancy walking back up the hill and explaining to Mr Wealthy that I had just driven his new Jaguar into the ocean, and that it was resting peacefully on the seabed. I took the opportunity to test each car's acceleration as I drove it back to the house. One of the other parkers nearly hit a couple of the guests who had drunkenly strolled down to collect their own car.

The girl, who had elected herself as head-honcho, got on the walkie-talkie and reported the incident to her boss. She was a lick, one of those people who constantly said things like, 'Lets do it, you guys!' and, 'You got it!' whenever Heather gave her instructions.

Her over-enthusiasm was positively cringe-worthy, and I felt like running her over with my 4.4 litre BMW jeep. She wasn't happy with me either, as I treated the cars as my own personal race toys. This may be the only time I would drive such elegant vehicles and I was fully intent on testing their power. I didn't give an American twinkie if she went complaining to Heather about my irresponsible child-like behaviour.

The wedding guests had all but left for their beds. We managed to avoid any calamities, like crashing into each other, and we kept all the cars 100% dry. Inspector Plod got away without having to arrest anyone. Albeit he did stare at the wall twiddling his thumbs with his back turned to the law-breaking folk behind him most of the time (I wanted to adopt him – he was so cute). And he was content for the night after consuming a truckload of free food. We each got paid $110 for a job well done, which meant it had been an extraordinary day for me money-wise. I felt no grief as I left the goody two shoes in the wake of dust from my convertible. But I would miss Inspector Plod.

On the way home, Heather asked me if I wanted to drive her car.

'Eh, no thanks.' I said.

Would ya go way out-a that. I was across into the driver's seat quicker than Sophie and Isabelle could change jobs. What a beast of a car. Ripping down narrow roads at 85mph, I knew this would be my future car – maybe if I sell enough copies of this book I'll be able to afford the ashtray and windscreen wipers for her.

We stopped back at base first, as she had to wait for one of the drivers who was out on a job. We chilled out and she fed me beers from the fridge. This day just couldn't get any better. But I was wrong. It could, and did; she also had crisps. Three longnecks later the driver came rolling into the yard. It was late, and I had a social gathering to attend. Heather told me to grab a beer for the road (which was illegal – told you she was cool) and off we went.

With just days before the big trip, I plucked up the courage to ask out the girl who worked at the halfway house on the golf course. She had been working there part-time for the summer. Normally, caddies were only permitted a drink and little tatty packet of cookies when they hit the tenth tee. But she had insisted earlier in the summer that I could take anything I wanted, from hot dogs to sandwiches. I asked Jim, who worked in the pro shop, about her a month ago and he said she had a boyfriend. I didn't believe him. There was something about the way he said it that seemed a bit suspect. Maybe it was because he and the rest of the staff fancied her, too, and they didn't want some pale Irish guy coming out and robbing their fantasy.

Since I only had a few more days on the Cape, I figured I would go for it. I could handle a bit of rejection at this stage. I hadn't got the balls to ask her out the first time, and when I was offered another round I had the ball teed up quicker than you could shout, fore! This time I would go through with it no matter how much wind I let out on account of nerves.

Approaching the snack shop the second time round, I was feeling a mix of excitement and terror. When my players had received, and paid for, their half-time refreshments, I stepped up. Summoning all the confidence I could draw upon I walked up, leaned against the counter, looked in her eyes while flashing a smile, and asked her if she had a boyfriend (I thought I was in a film). She smiled back.

'No.'

Oh Jasus. I might actually have a chance I thought to myself. She then asked why I wanted to know.

'Well,' I said, 'I was wondering if you'd like to come out with me tonight?'

There, I said it. My nerves had disappeared and my belly was free from all winged creatures. She turned me down – but not for your typical reasons. She was beginning college at the start of next week and had to visit her Dad who was living about two hours out the road (he was divorced from her Mother). She said she would have loved to have gone out with me but for this reason couldn't – at least it softened the blow. All I could do was think why the fuck didn't I ask her out earlier in the summer. And then I thought.

Jim. You're dead.

To help me get over my mini-heartbreak, Michael and I were to be treated to a seductive lap dance, performed for us exclusively by Erin and Sebastian. Each thought they could out-dance the other, so we became their willing judge and jury. The competition was only fierce and both parties performed exceptionally well with killer moves dispatched with natural fluency. Despite this there could only be one winner, and that was Erin. Sebastian just couldn't match her petite sexy movements and her amazing timing and efficiency (actually it had nothing to do with this; she was wearing hot pants with a skimpy top, and also threw in a light double fondle to top it off). Sebastian would have won otherwise.

Erin, not satisfied with this accolade alone, decided to put the final nail in Sebastian's coffin by publicly humiliating him by exposing his weaponry as she whipped down his pants. The judges, on seeing this atrocity, had a change of heart and reversed the decision, awarding lap dancer of the year to Sebastian. He later went on to demonstrate his prowess as a nude lap dancer for the embarrassed Laoibhse as a sort of belated birthday present.

Sebastian and Lisa had travelled to the States together as ex-boyfriend and girlfriend. They had broken up months before, but supposedly patched things up between them allowing a friendship to develop. Not quite. They had an explosive argument in the bathroom one evening when the whole house seemed to vibrate. We all thought the undertakers would have to be called to remove a body but who's we weren't sure.

With this out of the way, Lisa and John hooked up. They enjoyed each other's company for a few days until Sebastian, the sexy lap dancer, waltzed back onto the scene. The hating-each-other-with-a-vengeance couple reunited for a sort of farewell integrating of bodies and souls, or maybe as an intimate apology for the scolding fight. It came from nowhere, and it was a vicious sting for the Doc when he found out.

14

The Cape Cod sun
gets ready to set

For the first time all summer I was finally starting to make some serious cash. It was ironic that my pockets only now felt what it was like to carry real-life money just as my sojourn was about to end here. I concluded my reign as a caddy on a high note for two reasons.

Firstly, Max and myself were picked to caddy together for the first and only time, and I eventually managed to get one up on him. During the round I distracted him several times, which resulted in the loss of a putter head-cover for what was probably the most expensive putter you could buy. He became all panicky and kept asking if he should run back for it. This dilemma dulled his competence as a caddy (though it didn't stop road runner winning caddy of the year).

Secondly, I helped a woman golfer win the club match play championship that was held every year in late August. After eighteen holes she was dead square with her rival, and they had to play sudden death holes until one of them emerged victorious. It took a nail-biting three extra holes for her to finally wrap up the match. The tussle was watched by a whole load of spectators. I thought I was on the ladies pro-tour circuit as the gallery stayed glued to every stroke. A resounding applause rang through the muggy air when she tapped in the winning putt that sealed her triumph. Overcome with joy, she paid me double the normal rate, so the pair of us were exultant come the end of the day.

Every now and then, a weird incident would happen out of the blue. One night as Emma and Sheila were walking home after completing a strenuous evening shift at the restaurant, they had just arrived back, when they witnessed a sight that they really didn't want to keep watching. Across the road, an alleged drunk was indulging in a spot of self-gratification (mustn't have had much luck in Pufferbellies, poor chap). The girls ran into the house ASAP just in case he asked them for a hand. Reports were unclear as to his nationality. For the sake of our sight, we hoped in future he either hooked up with someone of the opposite sex, or had a nasty accident resulting in a most unfortunate de-nobing.

In other news, Jacob and Shauna were twice caught attempting to run away with a wheelie bin. The first time, Shauna jumped in, and Jacob ran down the road pissed as a fart trying to give her a good ride. They were stopped by a cop, who told Jacob that only trash was meant to be put in the bin. Much to Shauna's displeasure, he replied.

'But this is my trash.'

The second time it happened, the renegade couple were just about home and dry when who should spot them and force them to return the bin to its rightful place but the very same skulking officer. They managed to get away with a warning, and were politely asked to stop abducting the bin.

Parties were coming at us thick and fast as it was nearly September, but we were doing our best to 'Busch' them all. Nevaeh had romantic success two nights running: an Irish guy, and a canon-armed guy who worked in the liquor store. Nevaeh not only managed to smooch the nights away but also lived up to her kleptomaniac reputation by somehow stealing the American's new expensive sandals and his shiny-new red baseball cap. She was without doubt the most competent and skilled thief on the Cape. Along with this she spent most of the time ridiculing him and making him obey her every queer command (could have made for some very interesting scenarios in the bedroom had they made it that far).

Chris was finding other more cost-effective ways of getting his hands on some drink for our social galas. He crawled through an open window in one of the pubs in Hyannis (the name of which will remain a secret) and smuggled out bottles of vodka and an armful of beers on two separate occasions. These escapades provided Chris with the ammunition to trigger an inferno of merriment, as well as being a challenge to Nevaeh for the best boost award at the end of the month.

Anna experienced the dangerous side of the Cape when she got rat-arsed at one of the parties. She fell around the house puffing away at cigars (something she would never do), drinking anything that smelled of alcohol (that's where my aftershave went), and basically just let her deepest inhibitions roam free. Emma and Michael looked after her that night making sure, after much noisy protesting, that she got to bed in one piece.

The tables were turned the next night when Emma took her place as the resident fanatic and, with roles reversed, it was her sister's turn to put her to bed. Ah, the irony of it all.

Making the most of the days left we visited the beach as much as we could. It could be another year before we would be able to enjoy a swim in the ocean without our nipples falling off from the cold. I was out swimming with Lisa one day and something wasn't right. Something was lurking, waiting for its chance. It pounced. Pain struck. All it needed was an inch and it took its opportunity to inflict serious anguish.

Lisa was stung by a jellyfish. Writhing in pain, I suggested she should pee on it. But she looked most peculiarly at me. Obviously she hadn't seen that episode of *Friends*. To make it worse she had been stung on her shoulders and chest, so unless she was into some seriously kinky shit, that ruled me out. It took the effects of the sting about twenty minutes to wear off, though to her credit she chose to ride out the pain rather than performing the method I had suggested.

With all that cash I had made during the last week, Nevaeh and I decided to really go all out and threat ourselves to a first class meal in a posh, highfalutin restaurant. We chose the Black Cat, just down the road from where we lived. For once, we felt like living the good life and indulging in a little bit of extravagance. Michael and Emma were being treated to a slap-up feed by Emma's big sis for the hospitality she was shown. Since the five of us were dressed up and ready for some serious dining, we made it a party of five.

The meal got off to a humorous start even before the food was served. A fly was floating serenely, if somewhat unwelcomingly, in Emma's water. As she was going to hand it back to the waitress, she knocked it over, soaking Michael with her insect-infected drink. Instantly, the waitress exclaimed 'Jesus!' as if to say you foolish little girl. The five of us crooked our heads and looked at her when she gasped this. She was quite weird. Some of the things she said were unexpected and strange, which made the dinner all the more interesting. I think she looked on us as ignorant, snotty kids, who didn't deserve the same type of treatment as the rest of the more upper-class customers.

This didn't faze us much; we were too busy drooling over the thought of the scrumptious delicacies we were about to gorge. Nevaeh and myself agreed beforehand that we would share a whole Lobster between us. Then we thought, why not share a big bowl of mussels to start with, so that's what we did. The fish was delicious. The only thing we could have faulted was the madcap waitress, but she helped add a touch of comedy to the evening. No fishy meal would be complete without some double chocolate cake and ice cream that was to die for. Nevaeh almost did – if she hadn't have opened her trousers she probably would have burst. Taking into account the lack of respect that was shown to us, we somehow neglected to tip the waitress; silly us, we really should be more careful next time.

Three days. That's all the time we had left on the Cape. The summer had vanished from right under our noses. It was hard to believe that the three months were nearly at an end and we would soon be forced to leave. Everyone had grown to love Hyannis – it had become our home. Our time there had made us all happy. We went around with our heads held high; we were both confident and content. In many ways, Hyannis had changed our lives significantly; from the friends we had made to the lovers we had discovered. Our opinions and attitudes, too, were altered. The little, basic things in life were now appreciated, and people learned to accept others for who they were. It had been a life lesson, and an important one at that.

In just a few short days we would be taken from the world we had grown so accustomed to, that had supported and taken us in with open arms, where we felt we belonged. And it would disappear forever. People knew the inevitable was just over the horizon, and they mourned secretly for its passing. There were still holidays to look forward to, but they signalled the end of a chapter in our lives.

One night outside the liquor store, Nevaeh and I had sold the idea of a road trip to Bruce. After the animated presentation he was dying to jump into Stacy. We had christened the station wagon that, it seemed the most obvious name to give her. We now had four members in our posse. Jeanie and Jackie then booked their place in the car, but later were forced to pull out for financial reasons. After trying all the people we thought would be suitable and compatible to join us for the week, we had failed to find that last all-important recruit.

That Friday while we drove along in Mocha's jeep, I had a weird feeling about the car. So I got Mocha to drive over to the company to verify everything was ready for Monday morning. Our old friend was still there, Mumbles McHumdrum, and still rambling on about the weather and every other meaningless topic. I told him I had come to make sure all the loose ends were tied up for our trip.

Looking through the bookings he could find no evidence of a reservation for a station wagon on the first of September for a week. I assured him I had booked the car for that week, and had even been in a second time to reduce to rental-time from two weeks to one. The dopey lemon then informed me that they were closed on Monday because it was Labor Day, and followed this up by blaming me for any mistake that had been made. My face started to go fire-red, like Daffy Duck's when Bugs Bunny winds him up. I said to myself, 'calm down, he's just a prick with a fascination for telling strangers about the different types of clouds'.

Such gall to accuse me of screwing things up, when surely after booking the car for the first he could have told me they would be closed that day. This guy really was the pits. Unable to restrain myself I snapped that it couldn't possibly have been my fault and it was an obvious fuck-up on his behalf. I wasn't going to take any bullshit from this arrogant yaker. I told him, as blatantly as I could, that I needed the car for Monday morning as I had arranged my flights around this trip. Reluctantly he caved, and said I could collect it on Sunday afternoon, during the half-hour period he was scheduled to be in the office. Then he said that he should charge me for the extra day but wouldn't.

'Dead right you won't.' I replied.

What a dick. I think he won the head-wrecker of the summer award hands down. I was just relieved I had called in to check on the arrangements. Had things gone wrong, I couldn't have been held responsible for my actions.

With two nights left to make a lasting impression we were intent on having the most prodigious, record-breaking bashes we could marshal. There was a barbeque organised for later that night and a lot had to be done beforehand.

I continued to caddy, as I needed as much as I could earn before Monday. I planned on tomorrow being my last round, but the hangover next morning numbed my senses and would put pay to that. So, after what turned out to be my last round, I fled to the mall to buy presents for my family back home. I could afford to splash out a little with my recent good fortune. I ended up buying so much stuff that I was forced to go to one of the big outlet stores to buy a suitcase to hold all the gifts.

There was one particular shop in the mall that sold a selection of cool, far-out things, which was where I did most of my spending. They also sold funny gags, including fanny floss, which was actually for your bum. In America fanny means arse, and to this day I still don't know what the proper expression for fanny is in American terms. Anyway, I bought the floss for my Mam (which apparently shocked some people), as she always found that specific difference between the two languages amusing. When I had finished trudging round the mall picking up outlandish presents, I faced a long walk home.

Next on the agenda was the most important mission of all – burgers. I met Emma, Anna and Michael in the supermarket. We all forked out for burgers (which were remarkably cheap), baps, crisps and drinks. Michael and I stopped off in the liquor store to buy Mocha a big bottle of Absolute Vodka as a token of our appreciation for all he had done for us. He had become a true friend, and despite his own problems with Alice, he tried his level best to make us feel at home and help in any way he could. He even let me drive his jeep some evenings to fetch some refreshments of the liquid-sort, insisting that I go before he had time to think about it.

With all the necessary chores over and done with, we could finally relax into the bosom of that balmy evening. The barbeque was a hit, and set people up nicely for the cult ritual that would follow. The booze worship would last till the sun eventually popped its yellow head above the tall trees.

Nevaeh and Clare were down on the roster to work both Saturday and Sunday nights at the Christmas Tree Store. Taking a deep look inside their souls they carefully considered what course of action to take. On one hand, they could stock shelves for the night with a load of sombrero-wearing Mexicans, and on the other, they could be a part of what could be the best shindig so far. In the blink of an eye they had cracked open some Busch Light and were knocking it back like Armageddon was scheduled for tomorrow. Sorry Christmas Tree Shop, you'd just have to learn to survive without your sleepiest employees.

Our house was positively rocking. It had never hosted so many people, and was trying its best to cope. This surely was the epitome of what the summer was all about; enjoying your last weekend with all the great friends you had made along the way, doing what the Irish loved best.

The previous morning when I had come home from caddying, who was perched peacefully on the stool in the sitting room but none other than Deco. The wonderer had returned to see out the last days of the summer. To fly back all the way from Ireland for just a few days will show you the extraordinary passion and effect Cape Cod had on people. We were all hooked on the place and on each other and were determined to choke every last drop of pure unadulterated bliss that we could.

Deco may have regretted coming back over. The sin of falling asleep on the couch brought its own retribution. Three cruel barbarians carried out a sex change on the unsuspecting victim. Five minutes later, and without so much as a peep, he had become a beautiful young girl. The lipstick matched his outfit and the eye shadow really did bring out the colour of his eyes. A sight to behold when he did come out of his hibernation he would make some guy very, very happy.

The fiesta was to be spoiled with the arrival of the Hyannis Law Enforcement Department. Some of the neighbours had complained about the illegal noise levels. It was the first time since moving into Ocean Street that the cops had busted us. I suppose it was only fair. All the other Irish houses, at some point or other, had been invaded by these thwarters of craic. Events came to a premature climax (story of my life), but we still had tomorrow to look forward to.

The final twenty-four hours were upon us. It was sore heads all round when we woke that morning from the previous night's booze fest. People were slowly beginning to pack their bags through a barrage of bittersweet memories. It felt like the death of a way of life, and a certain part inside every one of us was dying, too. We thought the summer would never end, we thought we would be forever trapped inside this fantasy we had been living.

Jessica and Clodagh were getting ready for their weeklong excursion to the sunshine state of Florida. Accompanying them were Sarah, Renee, and the rest of their friends. One of the sons who owned Gringo's was also tagging along; Jessica used him as a slave for the week, making him do her laundry and every other job that had to be done – only thing for him.

They found a site on the Web that offered flights and accommodation in a three star hotel for seven nights, for a paltry $300. They immediately grabbed it with both hands (or even clicked with both fingers). This gave them an opportunity to top-up their fading tans and go home looking like exotic beauties. The girls also attended a Red Hot Chili Peppers concert in New York in style as they were chauffeured to the door in a stretch limo giving them that movie-star feeling.

Maria and Laoibhse were off to Cancun in Mexico to consort with some chicos-locos and live on cheap drink, while Sheila and Harry were going a little bit more sophisticated with a trip to New York. Jack and Alyssa had saved enough money to be able to afford something decent, so they chose a mix between Boston and New York staying in swanky hotels and enjoying a bit of pampering for seven or eight days. Deco, Brian and Jacob were attracted to the bright lights of Las Vegas where they would stay for three nights.

This was the great thing about America. There were so many different places to go to, and all types of holiday to choose from, and everyone picked the one that appealed to them most.

Out with a bang
(and a bust)

15

Michael and I were outside the rent-a-car company dead on the stroke of noon. We didn't want to give Mumbles anymore excuses. As we walked into the shop he made some snide comment, but we stood stern, insisting that we were there for our car. He wasn't best pleased that we were getting an extra day free of charge as he mentioned it a couple of times. True to form, he painstakingly went through the do's and don'ts involved in hiring a car. We tuned off and let him carry on until we could hear no more ranting. He was like a broken record that threw out babbling, dishevelled notes.

'Here are the keys, now remember all the things I told you, and be careful!' Mumbles said in a condescending manner.

'Ah sure don't worry about it, boy, the car will be safer with us than parked here,' we replied, as he shot us a cynical look.

Swiping the keys from his sweaty clutches the car was ours to do as we saw fit. We vaguely remembered him rattling on about a list of rules and conditions but we mustn't have been paying attention – our loss I suppose.

Since we had the car for an extra day we thought we might as well put it to good use. Michael, Sebastian, Sheila, Harry and I ventured out to a few of the bargain shops to see what sort of delights we could find. I was on a mission to buy a pair of sandals – I must have been the only pillock that walked around in runners all summer. But in shop after shop there was no sign of a decent pair of sandals.

Jumping into the car on our return from Fileens Basement, we began to drive off. There were two elderly women, one of them using a walking frame, slowly coming up behind the car. I started to drive away and the women began bawling and shouting insults at us. I don't know why they turned psycho – I was miles from hitting them. Harry turned around and gave them his own personal salute. Sticking his little finger to his mouth and his thumb to his ear he yelled back to the grannies.

'Call me!'

I had never seen handbags being waved so vigorously. Good old Harry never failed to get a laugh out of people.

In the end, I bought an overpriced pair of Nike Air Moses for the trip, which, incidentally, I never even wore. We also went to visit Mocha and other places of interest in Hyannis (Wendy's). Stacy had to be warmed-up before her big journey the next day.

Our last night on the Cape was a fitting finale. Dinner was eaten early so there was ample time for drinking. It was to be our gala send-off to Pufferbellies – the club that had treated us so well and showed us so many great times. There wasn't an Irish person in Hyannis that didn't show up at the club that night. Even Jessica and Clodagh, the 'not bothered girls', managed to make an appearance. Another unfaltering performance, and everyone got a chance to find out about people's plans and to say their final farewells.

Nevaeh and Deco arrived with about twenty minutes to go. They had been immersed in chat all evening in the car in front of the house. High heels once again swung by to torment Nevaeh. When she got into Pufferbellies one of them snapped off, turning her into a sort of hop-a-long stooge.

Everyone assembled on the dance floor for the last two songs – the most important ones. In full voice, we sang *Beautiful Day* and the national anthem louder and harder than we had ever done before. The raw emotion poured out as we put our hearts and souls into singing these cherished tunes.

A big crowd of revellers went back to Nantucket Street to try to end the night on a high. For us it was the night of the *Six Deadly Hoists*. There was a famous poster on the wall which I had always wanted to own. It was a picture of eleven scrawny Irish workers sitting on a steel beam hundreds of feet in the air overlooking New York City while on their lunch break.

Towards the end of the night, Nevaeh told me to go outside and she would take the picture down and pass it out the window to me. All on for this, I took my leave and snuck out. Somehow, Nevaeh managed to take this fairly large poster off the wall without being seen, and slipped it out the open window to where I was waiting.

Nevaeh wasn't finished. She had gotten a taste for this adrenaline-induced activity and wanted more. The picture wasn't enough. She needed more things to nick from the house I deplored from the very start. She managed to sneak a *Blade 2* video, a packet of cigarettes, an Irish flag, a hat and a disposable camera through the window and into my grasp. I think that was sufficient payback for any disagreements that had occurred between us.

For the second time of asking the cops once again sent our party to an early grave. One particular cop was wearing hot pants; he must have been the gay member of the squad. Nevaeh hurt her feet as normal, and she convinced the 'opposite team' policeman to hold a bag of ice to her swollen ankle, while someone took pictures of this hilarious image. This topped off the night in great fashion. It was time to sleep, for tomorrow our grand adventure across America would begin.

It was strange to think that the summer as we knew it had come to an end. It left an empty, lamenting feeling in your stomach. We were in the process of packing our bags for the very last time. Who would have guessed we'd miss such a trivial habit so much. We were sad. Even though we were going on holiday for a week we were sad.

We planned on leaving at noon, but after the amount of drink we had the night before, that delayed our start a couple of hours. Nevaeh was busy getting all her stuff together across the road while Michael and I were making last minute checks that we had everything. We tried to convince Deco to come with us on our travels, but he had decided to work for a few days and then head off to the gambling capital with two of the lads.

With that, John asked rhetorically, for the benefit of a bit of encouragement, whether he should go on the trip. We told him to hurry up and start packing his cases, that he was more than welcome to join us. After a couple of minutes of indecision and weighing things up (he wasn't the most spontaneous guy in the world) he finally decided to abandon caution and become the fifth and final passenger in the adventure wagon.

I drove over to pick up Nevaeh and her gear. She had just sold a bike to her landlord. It wasn't just any old bike. Nevaeh had topped off her kleptomaniac ways in style. Coming home from Main Street the other night she spotted a lone bike stranded outside one of the bars on Ocean Street. With catlike stealth she swiped the new bike that lay helpless on the cold, dark pavement. It was tough-going bringing both bikes home, but she made it eventually.

Take a bow, Nevaeh. She had pulled off the ultimate robbery and got away with it. What a pro. We could all surely learn a few things from the greatest thief that ever strolled the amiable streets of Hyannis. For her talents she was to receive a cheque for $70 from her landlord, despite the bike being worth a lot more. Her skills lay in the art of burglary, not negotiation.

When we had all our belongings packed into Stacy, it was time to motor. All the lads in the house came out to see us off. Not normally one for soppy goodbyes I couldn't help but be moved by the emotional scene that was unfolding.

The four of us made the rounds, kissing the girls and giving the guys, well, man-hugs. Tears of sadness were shed and regrets were felt at the impending departure from our friends' lives. We had all grown close, so being separated was like losing a bit of yourself. Emma wept for the loss of her boyfriend, wishing she could come, too. But instead had to stay and work through a surge of doubts. Advice for our safety was dispensed, and they wished with all their hearts that we got home alive and well.

As we turned out onto the road from the driveway, everyone was waving wildly, as if we weren't going to see them again for a lifetime. Our hearts skipped a beat as we realised how special this was. It was an incredible feeling to know people can care so much about you and how close you can become. It will be remembered as one of the happiest moments of, not just my summer, but of the other three people who sat with me in the car. A quick pit stop to collect Bruce and have a few pictures taken with his friends and we were off in search of the wildest adventures America could toss our way.

And hopefully there would be many.

Road Trip here we go!

16

Four different counties, five completely different personalities, and, for those astrologists among you, five different sun signs. But all were intent on having the time of their lives. It made for the perfect blend of characteristics that would surely enhance our enjoyment of the trip.

We couldn't have asked for a nicer day to begin our journey. The sun beamed downed on us as we opened the windows and let our hair blow in the wind (well Nevaeh did, the rest of us had no hair). Our first port of call was of the essence. Stacy didn't come equipped with a CD player so we had to stop by the mall one last time for an adaptor – since we already had a portable player. Four dollars each for the adaptor, which enabled you to connect a CD player to the tape deck, and we were sorted (I never even knew there was such a device). With that little matter taken care of, we got back onto the highway and headed towards the horizon.

Our plan for the week was to hit Niagara Falls. Then we would head due south to Philadelphia where Erin would put us up for the night and, if we were lucky, throw a bit of a bash to celebrate our arrival. That was the plan, but whether it would actually come to fruition was another question. We drove out of Cape Cod and onto the menacing roads of America. We managed to avoid going into Boston by heading north around the city.

We decided to spend the first night in Vermont, a supposedly beautiful mountain retreat. On the way we got lost and came within touching distance of Salem. This is the famous town that hosted the witch trials in the seventeenth century; the witches were subsequently burned at the stake for their beliefs.

Salem was nothing special. It seemed relatively quiet. I think all the witches were inside stirring their stews. We parked in the town to grab a bite to eat; we had been driving for a good while and were hungry. There was an Irish bar on one of the street corners, but it didn't open till seven. An hour and a half away – that put us out of contention.

A witch shop stood next door to the pub so we decided to have a gander. They sold everything you would expect – crystals, jewellery, brooms, and all sorts of witch memorabilia. I bought a sign for myself and a T-shirt for my little sis. The girl who worked there was herself an authentic witch, not to mention a fairly attractive one at that. I had never met a real life witch before so I had to mark the occasion with a photo. One of the lads obliged. I would now forever have the sweet face of this sexy ghoul on my wall – that's if she actually came out in the picture. She recommended somewhere we could eat, and, on hearing the restaurant's name, we were out the door and heading to the Salem Brewery. For this kind deed we hoped that she escaped the inconvenience of being burned to death on a pole at sunrise.

The Brewery was lively and bright. The five of us ordered our food – mostly different varieties of chips, and sampled some of the local home-brews. After satisfying our cravings it was back to the car, which we had parked across the road from a witch museum, free of charge. The Mayor of the town (don't ask me his name, we couldn't even pronounce the thing) had declared it a no parking-fee day due to some obscure achievement of his (maybe he had caught and killed a witch his ancestors had missed – hopefully Sabrina). We would have preferred a no beer-fee day, but parking was fine, too.

'Oh fuck lads we're in trouble.'

A cop stood out from behind a tree and into the middle of the street, signalling for us to pull over. We had just come off the Highway and had been caught speeding on the off-ramp. To rub salt in the wounds, we had taken the wrong turn. Rolling down my window I prayed he wouldn't smell the homemade stout on my breath from dinner.

'Do you realise you were doing 40mph on a 25mph road?' the officer sternly asked.

Jesus, I was full sure I had been going quicker than that.

'No officer, I didn't realise I was going at such a speed, I'm very sorry about that, it was totally unintentional,' I replied apologetically.

I had read that it was in your best interests to be very respectful and courteous to the law enforcement in the States. Otherwise you ran the risk of being broken-in, in a bad way, at the local jail. They were the people in command, and demanded you treated them as such. I gave him my license and papers from the rent-a-car company. Sitting patiently in the car for five minutes the cop once again approached the window after making the relevant phone calls from his cruiser.

'I'm going to leave you off this time, but I'm giving you a warning.'

'Ah, officer that's very kind, I'll make sure to slow down in future.'

Me bollocks.

That was too close for comfort, but we avoided the standard fine for a speeding violation, which in itself was a relief.

We spent the next few hours driving towards Vermont. We made a 'deoch-drip' at a large, supermarket-type liquor store along the way. Typically, Michael was the last one to leave the shop. As he was loading the car with booze, he put his backpack on the roof so he could fit the drink in. Once he had finished loading-up we set off. As we picked up speed, Michael asked with the greatest of ease.

'Did I put my bag back in the car?'

We all thought for a second. Next thing, the bag rolled down the back window, over the boot, and onto the road. Again, with the most nonchalant of attitudes, Michael replied to his earlier enquiry.

'Hmmm, maybe I didn't.'

We all broke out into fits of hysterics as we watched the bag belting down the off-ramp at a hundred miles an hour, while the following cars swerved to avoid it. We pulled over and Michael hopped out and ran after the speeding backpack (bags seemingly were immune to speeding tickets). It was a fantastic photo opportunity. John laughed so hard that he couldn't control himself, and let out the foulest fart any of us had ever come in contact with. We had to open all the windows and aerate the car for an hour afterwards.

We knew we must have been coming close to Vermont as the flora was beginning to change and tall green forests came to the fore. The roads, too, becoming steep climbs followed by dizzying down hills.

Freewheeling took over giving your feet a chance to relax. Darkness had fallen. I didn't relish the thought of driving on these gargantuan motorways in pitch black on my first day. We arrived at nine on the button, which begged the question. What now?

I had a plan up my sleeve. I shared it with the lads but all it led to was a backlash of pessimism from every corner. I proposed that we head down to a pub or party of some sort, as there was a university here, get to know a few students, and bunk up with them for the night. This however wasn't enthusiastically received.

We decided to call into one of the massive frat houses that you see on TV that accommodate dozens of students attending the university. Parking the car outside a Sigma Beta Fata Lata Nanna Banana Anna Kournikova Canna Buda Wanna Jamma Mamma Gamma house, we trotted over and rang the bell. A middle-aged man opened the door, which hadn't been what we were expecting.

'Em. Hello,' we said tentatively. 'We were wondering if you would be able to recommend any places that we could get a drink, either in a bar, nightclub, or all out widow-shattering house party?'

Well, we left the last bit out. He explained how to get to the town, which wasn't far, where there were a few bars to choose from. Cool. Rolling down the ski-slope of a hill we quickly arrived in the small town of Burlington. Scenically, Vermont was rousing. I would like to experience it in the depths of winter, when the snows arrive and transform this sleepy town into a bustling ski resort.

Walking down the street in search of a lively bar, and our beds for the night, two girls walked out from a pub ahead. I quickly grabbed their attention. Who knew how many other students we would find. There didn't seem to be many out on the town. In my best Irish accent I asked the girls if there was anywhere decent to drink, or any parties we could crash. They were thrilled at the fact we were from Ireland, and after a little while, asked us where we were staying.

'Ah sure Jasus girls to tell ya the truth, we're being forced to sleep in the car tonight. Tis shocking but that's how it goes, ya knoo.'

Unhappy to hear of our sleeping arrangements they kindly asked if we wanted to stay with them for the night.

Ah ha!

'I knew we could do it,' I whispered to the doubting Thomases.

Then they remembered that they had to consult their friends who shared the apartment with them. So they gave us their number and told us to give them a call in about forty-five minutes.

'Oh sure grand, we'll do that girls.'

We grabbed a quick pint in the pub and then headed up to the university car park. We amused ourselves with a brief interlude of football and a Rolling Rock beer before we rang the girls.

Pulling up at a shop-cum-fast-food joint we spotted a payphone. The required time had elapsed. We didn't want to seem overly eager so we gave it an extra twenty minutes or so. Good news was to follow the call, as they had agreed between them to take in the five stray Irish – we had beaten the car for the first night. Incensed, Stacy intended on settling the scores. We couldn't get her started when we got back in. It took us a while to realise that the stick wasn't set to the correct option. Once we had adjusted the automatic, she roared like a lion – well maybe a screamapillar, but that's beside the point.

The next morning we had to be up early. All the girls in the house were starting college – that was why the pubs had been so quiet the night before. We had charmed our hosts for a short while, had a few beers, and settled into bed at a respectable hour. They made up beds for us in their large sitting room, and Nevaeh and myself dived on the double bed that was neatly laid out on the floor. We had been sleeping buddies all through the summer, including twice as I was on the verge of sleep and she drunkenly bounded on my bed, loafing me in the head – the good old days. We thanked them for their hospitality and headed off for our first day in college.

I had always wanted to see what it was like to go to university in America. We moseyed around the huge campus, stopping for free coffee on the way to look for our new class. When we found what we were looking for – animal science, we entered our building. Just inside the doors, a framed life-size polar bear stood commanding attention in a huge glass case. I'm not sure if it was fake or stuffed – another photo opportunity.

Our class was held in a massive theatre that resembled every other one you'd see in films like *Road Trip* (coincidence) and the like. Unlike Ireland, from the first day college is taken very seriously and to them it is a big deal. There is no such thing as missing a class because you had a hankering for a chicken baguette, a pint of Guinness and a game of pool. Being fond of grand introductions and ceremonies, every single lecturer took a minute or two to give the class a little insight into their lives.

'Hi guys! My name is Taylor Chad Billy-Bob, and I come from the town of

Inbred, in the great state of Nebraska!
Are any of you guys from there? No.
Okay that's fine! Anyway when I was
just six-years old, my Daddy ran off
leaving me to look after my Mom, who
always used to call me Elmer – just like
my favourite cartoon character! Wasn't
he cute with his little stutter? You
know I used have me one of those!
Until my Mom beat it out of me that
is.'

Please.

We don't want to hear about your dysfunctional
family, or the fact that your birthday is on the same day
as April Fools. And we definitely don't care that you
have an inoperable mole on the inside of your left bum
cheek.

Once the shortened life-stories had been so
eloquently told, the students were invited to the
bottom of the class to indulge in free drinks (non-
alcoholic of course), cookies and chocolate. Nevaeh and
Michael stayed in their seats while Bruce and myself
(John had gone to find a phone to change his flights)
went down to see what we could scab. We came back up
with handfuls of different types of tasty homemade
buns and drinks for everyone. We were shot a few
disapproving looks by members of staff and students
alike, but they weren't trying to survive for a week on
repossessed treasures and lumps of fat in a bap.

After we were given our assignments for the
semester, it was time to leave Vermont. Thanks be-to
Jasus, because unlike the striking landscape, the
students in that college were the ugliest sons of bitches
we had ever seen. The girls looked like guys, and the

guys looked like monkeys with virtually all of them sporting some sort of facial hair. Several had such aberrant styles that they would have surely gotten 'crow-barred' had they have gone somewhere more chic like New York, or Alabama, for the weekend.

Heading west towards Niagara Falls, we soon realised we weren't going to get there on Tuesday, the second day. On the way to our next destination, which was as yet undecided, we visited a city called Manchester. To say it was a kip was paying it a complement. We stayed long enough to fill Stacy with petrol and then split as quick as we could.

The seating arrangements in the car remained fairly constant. Michael liked the passenger seat as it allowed him keep sketch for police while enjoying his suds-lunch. Nevaeh carved her name in the middle of the backseat. She demanded to be sat between the muscle-shaped physiques of Bruce and John. 'Take your top off', became the official road trip saying. Nevaeh piped this so much – especially when the weather became hot, or she had accidentally on purpose spilled a drink on the boys – that it became ingrained in our heads. John even began whispering it as he entered the early stages of sleep.

The motorways were long and monotonous. The threat of falling asleep at the wheel, due to the lack of stimulation or bends in the road to hold your attention, was a strong possibility. That was the first and only day we had to deal with rain while driving, and it came down like a monsoon. Even with the wipers on full speed, it was impossible to see more than a few yards ahead. It continued like this for about half an hour, before turning into a drab and irritating drizzle. For the sake of our sanity Michael suggested going across the mountains, which would eventually take us to Niagara Falls. Stresses faded and tensions eased as we cruised along forest-lined roads that sometimes parted to reveal beautiful lakes hidden from the attention of passers-by. This was a million times more pleasurable than the car-infested freeways we had just been on.

We passed quaint mountain towns that exuded tranquillity and peacefulness – apart from one noisy blip that smashed the deadening silence. As we lay waiting for the traffic lights to turn green, we caught sight of a *Fast And The Furious* type car beside us. We did what any other free and mad bunch of lads would do, and that was to challenge the electrifying green piece of engineering magic that was directly opposite.

I started to rev Stacy's engine. Two guys with chiselled, handsome appearances immediately glanced over in our direction. I think we had the element of surprise over them as their expressions dropped – it was fear, had to be. In retaliation, the beast of a car came back with her own blend of deafening, malicious screams that would have made Eddie Irvine quiver at the knees. Determination and focus lit up our faces. The lights went green. We shot off in envious fashion only to realise that our opposition had turned left onto another road. What a chicken. That would teach him not to mess with the incalculable power of Stacy the Station Wagon in future.

Examining the map, we voted that we'd visit Lake Placid – mainly because we thought it had some connection with the film that starred Brendan Gleeson and the monster-like bloodthirsty crocodile. Lake Placid was on the top of the Adirondack Mountains in the state of New York, despite being hours away from the actual city. Without doubt, it was by far the most scenically breathtaking place we visited. We toured the small town that had twice held the Winter Olympics.

We came across intimate wooden pubs and log cabin restaurants where couples could sit beside the fireplace, sipping hot chocolate or a glass of wine, while staring lovingly into each other's eyes. It was an extremely romantic setting, appropriately separated from the hectic hustle and bustle of the real world. We decided to avoid these places (our relationships were of a different kind). Instead we took a look in some of the cute, independently run shops that hadn't as yet been taken over by heartless money-grabbing corporations that seemed to own and ruin everywhere else. We bought some mementos and gifts for family and friends back home.

Since there was no university, we were forced to look for paying accommodation. We tried a couple of places but they were well out of our league. We had one left to try before resigning ourselves to a night in the car. Stepping into the attractive log cabin that was the reception area, I was approached by a friendly-looking woman. I asked her how much for the five of us for the night, and braced myself for the worst. Inside I leaped for joy as she said it would be $13 each for our own cabin. We could definitely afford to pay for such a privilege. She was nice and outgoing and recommended some places where we could eat and drink. We asked her about the likelihood of seeing bears. She told us that there were many of them in the area and sightings and encounters with these wild animals were common. We desperately wanted to catch a glimpse of one in the flesh. Sadly, we never did get to see any of these magnificent beasts in action.

The mini-resort consisted of about fifteen charming log cabins and, just to make our day, literally outside our front door was a cabin, that was, in fact, a sauna. Well fuck me, you couldn't ask for more. The views were mind-blowing, and we were just across the road from the stunningly laid-out eighteen-hole golf course. Our hosts made us feel very welcome. We were provided with a pull out bed, along with the two double beds that already adorned the room. Once we were settled in, it was off with the clothes and on with the sauna suits. We each grabbed a couple of beers and went for some bone-warming therapy. Half an hour later we had built up a sufficient appetite and went in search of dinner.

We just about made it to the local Chinese restaurant before they shut. Even up a mountain, in the back end of nowhere, the Chinese had managed to open a restaurant. Was there anywhere left they hadn't colonised with their takeaways. We tried a few places to get a drink but, like everywhere else, they wouldn't allow Nevaeh in, as she was underage (if the owners only knew she could drink most, if not all, of the regulars under the table). It didn't really matter as we were all shattered from the last few nights. So we agreed on watching a bit of TV and having a few jars to help us sleep. Turned out we didn't need much assistance and were asleep by one.

The next morning we woke bright and early with a spring in our step after a satisfying few hours' shuteye. We drove over to Lake Placid, a short distance away. It was a warm, bright, thinly veiled cloudy day, instilled with serenity – just like you'd imagine from a mountain hideaway. It looked surreal. A majestic deep shade of blue stretched out lifeless as far as the eye could see. We stood in awe gazing at the tall green trees that perfectly framed the lake on all sides. It had all the ingredients for a unique photo, which we tried our best to depict. Plush houses dotted the lake water's edge, with private docks where they could moor their boats. Decks on top consisted of barbeques and seating, so they could entertain friends and family during the summer, while gazing on this incredible natural feature as they tucked into their chicken breasts.

In the distance was a water trampoline, probably owned by one of the rich homes. Feeling inspired by my surroundings, I put forward the idea of swimming out to the trampoline. The lads looked at me as if I had been drinking all morning. In the end, apart from John who was still full from breakfast, the four of us stood on the dock wearing nothing but underwear and cheeky smiles. John accepted the responsibility of being the cameraman, and snapped us as we fearlessly leaped into the blue lagoon.

'Oh fuck, that's cold!' we yelled as our heads bobbed to the surface.

We underestimated the distance from the dock to the trampoline. Because it was a clear water lake we began to get very tired halfway there. It was lucky that there were houses on the shoreline. We had to rest, as we were unable to swim anymore. When we finally reached the multicoloured trampoline, we were panting like dogs in heat. We lay down for a while on the jumping platform. When we were fit and recovered we bounced away till we clumsily collided into each other crashing to the springy surface. We endured the same struggle on the way back and were glad to have returned alive. Although, it would have made a riveting tale to tell the tourists as they looked beneath the surface trying to locate our bodies while enjoying their glass bottom boat ride. Back on dry land, there had been enough drama in the town of Lake Placid and it was time to move on.

Analysing the map we had bought, Bruce pointed out that Syracuse was on our route. They had a really good football team and he proposed that we stay there for the night. As no one could come up with any better suggestions we settled on this university-city as our next stop.

Syracuse was a nice place, and seemed a lot livelier than Burlington, which could only be a good thing. We arrived during the day this time, which meant we saw the city in all its splendour. We stopped two girls who were walking home from college and asked them the best place to find some girls. One of them, who, was a pretty blonde, turned to her friend, who, was a pretty blonde.

'Well there's my friend here.'

At least they were a bit of craic, unlike the quieter, not-so-attractive students back in Vermont. They told us about a few bars that would be good that night and confirmed there would be crowds of people out on the tear.

We anchored the station wagon in a feeless car park, making sure it had sufficient vegetation to hide us as we answered nature's calls. 30-packs of Rolling Rock, which had become the official road trip drink, mobbed the boot. We knocked back these lovely, yet particularly gassy beverages, while we tried to come up with a plan for the night ahead. Running empty on ideas, we thought we'd hit the local bar for some inspiration.

On the way, Nevaeh was dying to use the jacks. We approached a frat house with a couple of guys standing outside. She ran up to them and begged to use their toilet. But they were totally against her entering the house, and refused her access. At this point she was in a fowl humour. Earlier in the day she was bursting to go, but I couldn't get off the freeway. Eventually, when

I did succeed in finding an off-road, we were unceremoniously charged $15 just to leave the feckin' road we were on. It had been the most expensive piss this century. Although she managed not to wet herself, she did however get sick from ther episode, and suffered from pains for most of the day.

All of a sudden, a gaggle of girls who lived beside the frat house were heading up the stairs of their own flamboyant home. She darted up to them, almost in tears, and pleaded with them to let her use their facilities. They allowed her, and I've never seen anyone run into a house as quick as she did that night.

With that little niggling problem taken care of, it was off to the pub. Along the way, a gang of girls were using an umbrella to shield them from the heavy downpours that were thumping us. So Nevaeh, still in no mood to be messed with, ran up and jumped under their brolly. Wondering who this mad yoke was, Nevaeh told them we were on a road trip, and seeking out a watering hole for the evening. They invited us to the bar where they were going. Since they knew the bouncers personally, they said they'd have no problem in convincing them to let in Nevaeh, who was only twenty (Bruce was the same age but he came loaded with his older, similar-looking brother's passport). The plan worked and we all got in, and I might add, free of charge.

Inside, the bar was thronged with students and the atmosphere was bubbling. We had eaten here earlier in the day when it had been a restaurant. Now it looked like a totally different place altogether. We were delighted to hear from the girls that it was flip night. A coin was flipped, and if you guessed the outcome of the toss correctly, the drink was on the house, and if you were wrong, you only had to pay normal price for it.

With five Irish people in the vicinity, the bar would surely pay for this most original of gambling games.

The three guys and myself were in deep discussion about the trip so far, and laughed as we reminisced about the summer. Nevaeh came over some time later. She told me that one of the girls, who had helped us get in, liked me. Nevaeh pointed her out.

'Hmmm, not bad.'

But I was hanging out with the lads enjoying the simple pleasures and I was in no mood to go wooing some girl. So I told Nevaeh to pull her for me – save me the trouble. She agreed, and went on her merry way. To our complete surprise one of the bouncers came over and bought us all a shot of Jameson. I don't think he had met that many Irish before and wanted to demonstrate his affection for our race. We told him that that was the best thing he could have bought an Irish person and the gesture was much appreciated.

I think I paid for one drink the whole night – thank you tails, you never let me down. But Bruce was becoming very agitated as he lost time after time. What a night! We were totally smashed on next to nothing (except Bruce), which worked out well because we had next to nothing. Once we managed to find Nevaeh (who was off gallivanting with some guys), it was back to the girls' house. They had kindly offered to take us in for the remainder of the night.

Walking back to the house, Nevaeh and myself began our own little rugby match on the grass, without the use of a ball. We dunked each other several times on the ground until we lost all feeling in our legs. There was an intercom on the side of the road, which students could use if they got into any trouble. This was a twenty-four hour emergency line that was permanently manned by an employee of the company – in case some screeching student was being chased by a maniac in a *Scream* mask and thought it would be a good idea to have a wee conversation with some anonymous voice at the end of the line before being gutted and hung up on an old oak tree. John, trying to be a hard (drunken) Paddy, ran over, pressed the button, and ran away.

'Hello can I help you, are you alright?' came the urgent voice at the other end.

'Ah ye, I'm grand, I just thought I'd ring and say hi.' I drunkenly replied.

'Are you actually in trouble?'

'Em, no, but I'd like to say you're doing a terrific job.'

'Well I'm afraid this is strictly for emergencies only.'

'It is an emergency, I have no drink left.'

She wasn't very supportive of my problem – so much for a helpline.

Home sweet home, we had arrived at our new lodgings for the next few hours. Mad Eejits 3 – Car 0. They had a large pull out bed in the living room and a couple of chairs that reclined. The girl, who fancied me, asked if I wanted to stay upstairs with her. Even though I was drunk, I was surprised at this offer. For one, I didn't know her name – though not important, and secondly, I hadn't spoke one word to her the whole evening, even when we were walking home. I was too caught up bantering with the mysterious voice down the telephone line. Despite these irrelevant discrepancies, I accompanied her upstairs to her bedroom. There was a bed, and beside it a couch that looked like it could be used as a bed.

'I don't have to sleep on that do I?' I asked pointing to the couch.

'Not if you don't want to.'

'Ah fuck no, the bed is fine by me.'

Within no more than a minute of getting into bed, I had fallen asleep. To be perfectly honest I was more interested in getting a few hours' kip than the girl that lay beside me. I felt an arm tapping me on the shoulder and a voice whispering as I was awoken.

'Are you awake?'

'Eh ye, ye, of course I am.' I sleepily but unconvincingly replied.

Damn it, she had woken me up. She must have been in the mood. This insatiable insomniac had destroyed my ambition for a dreamy, uninterrupted night's sleep. During the night I had to go to the toilet badly, but I didn't know where the door was. It was dark and I was dizzy. I felt along the wall and finally found the door. 'Jesus Christ', I moaned as I was approached by a handful of doors (it was like a TV game show from Japan where, if you opened the wrong door, there would be a tiger standing behind it waiting to rip you to shreds, or a morbidly fat woman bent over not wearing so much as a stitch, resigning you to permanent blindness).

'Which one is the fuckin' jacks?'

I decided to start trying them. The first one was locked. As I was noisily trying to open it, a girl's voice from within whispered loudly.

'Who's that!'

Shit, better find it quick. The second one I tried was the Promised Land. I immediately locked the door behind me in case the irate girl tried to knee cap me with a baseball bat. She stood at her doorway, with a nasty look, as I came out of the bathroom.

'Eh, sorry about that!' I cheerfully said as I strolled back to my room. Unimpressed, she spoke not a word and went back to her bed.

The next morning, she (I still had no idea of her name) had to be up at half seven. As my bed partner was getting dressed my flip-beaten eyes opened and I observed the girl I had spent the night with. She was still pretty. The beer goggles hadn't cruelly eluded me.

'Listen, thanks for letting us stay here.' I said sincerely, and she said not to mention it.

I think she expected me to get up with her. But instead, I told her to have a nice day, and once she had left the room I went back to sleep. I was jolted from my slumber a while later by loud knocking from Nevaeh. Bollocks, I thought, time to get up. She left her email address and a note saying how much she had enjoyed our company and was honoured to have met us. Not thinking straight we all forgot to take her address and off we toddled.

On the way to Niagara, a sign for Rochester caught my eye on the motorway. I had heard this place mentioned a few times and, as far as I could remember, it was meant to be big, one of the main cities in New York. We all thought, sure why not. It was so invigorating visiting all these different places, as most of them were distinctive in their own way.

The city was congested with high-rise buildings and roads that went in every possible direction. The good weather helped flatter the city. The sun created shadows that blended nicely with the light and everywhere looked peaceful. We were struck by the shortage of life; only a handful of people walked the bright streets. We were on the lookout for a car park, but more importantly, somewhere to eat. In the end we had to park in some weird place at the back of run-down buildings. We walked across an open space between the buildings, where it was just concrete, no flowers or grass or anything to help give life to this bleak, blank stone park.

Strangely, there were no shops or restaurants on the main road, just bland buildings that were probably offices – must be where all the people were hiding out. We asked a couple of folk if there was a mall around, but they weren't much help. They seemed incapable of answering the question, curious. We walked for a while and found a small mall with a couple of floors. There were a few shops and one of them was a Burger King upstairs. We tread across the mostly deserted shopping centre to get our lunch. There was an unusual vibe in the town and the atmosphere was spooky. Everyone we encountered seemed to be operating in slow motion, similar to zombies. The cashiers were lifeless as they took our money and handed us our burger and chips. Nothing emotional about them, it was like they were all dead or brainless. They could move but weren't capable of expressing feelings of any type.

Halfway through the meal, I went to the toilet. But I couldn't go. The seat was like sitting on a stone wall – without wearing any trousers. I could hear happy music that they play in a madhouse to try and cheer people up (but drove them deeper into the depths of depression instead) seeping out the speakers. I could feel myself slowly becoming insane so I hurried to get the rest of the gang to head; they were relieved.

Rochester looked to be draining the life out of its people. We imagined the rulers of the city putting special serum in the water system to achieve this zombie nation. Protruding above the top of the buildings ahead was, what appeared to be, an alien tower. It freaked us out just looking at it – that's where the aliens monitored all their mindless victims, we thought. This place was just too eerie. So as fast as we could we made it back to the car. We had become desperate to get out. It was having a negative effect on us and, we knew if we stayed any longer, we risked becoming like these poor souls that had no say in their demise.

The roads that led through Pennsylvania were uncannily similar to those in the film, *Jeepers Creepers*. The houses, too, looked the same as those in the movie. We took a fleeting look at each as we passed to see if there was any suspicious activity going on. I had been saying that all we needed now was to see that big rusty brown yoke that the evil man-come-bat drove. Approaching the next bend, what came speeding round the corner, managing to scare the bejesus out of us, but a fuckin' replica of the brown yoke. How I didn't crash into a field I'll never know. We just stared at each other, gobsmacked at the ghostly coincidence that had just happened. I leaned a bit heavier on the accelerator from then on.

We had a bit of trouble getting to Niagara Falls that day. We had stopped in McDonalds for some lunch just like we did every other afternoon cause it was all we could afford. The dollar menu, and free drinks they let us pinch, really kept us going. After lunch we took a wrong turn somewhere along the way and, an hour later, we had come full circle and returned to McDonalds – McFlurry anyone? When we did get our bearings, we took another wrong turn and, instead of heading towards Buffalo, which was on the border with Niagara, we passed by a checkpoint on the other side of the road.

Not realising we had just entered Canada we came to another checkpoint, this time on our side. We told them we had taken a wrong turn and got here by accident. We were a little concerned they wouldn't allow us back into America because there had been talk of J1s not being permitted to cross the Canadian border and then re-enter the States. They weren't best pleased and demanded we go in and show our passports. We spent the best part of a few minutes in Canada, just enough time to show the relevant documents and for Michael to take a dump in the little outhouse. At least something good came of it.

Despite these setbacks we arrived in Canada once again, only this time we had reached our intended location, Niagara Falls. Showing our passports for the second time that day, one of the checkpoint control people took it upon himself to give us a little pep talk. This consisted mostly of slagging off the Yanks and telling us about the war that took place between the two countries many years ago, when many brave Canadians had lost their lives. I noticed during his speech that the Canadians seemed to despise the Americans as much as we disliked the Brits. It seemed it was all down to a war that had left incurable scars. The Falls were just across the border, and we thanked the friendly American-hating Canadian for all his helpful advice.

The Falls exist in both America and Canada. The whole time we had been in Cape Cod we were urged not to bother with the American side, and instead to cross the border where it was far more impressive. Jesus, were they right. Niagara town was pulsating with the sounds of laughter and excitement from the many tourists. The buildings were a collage of vivid colours and flashing lights, and the streets were alive with attractions. It was like a mini-Blackpool or a multi-mini Disney World. We checked into a hotel right smack bang in the middle of Main Street. After trying a few other places without success, once again, we had somehow managed to unearth a cheap and convenient place to stay.

It was expensive to bring the car to see the falls. We had to fork out $4 each, which hurt. It was worth it, they were a wonderful sight. As the water cascaded down the Falls, it created a huge cloud of spray that hung indefinitely in the air. We strolled the promenade taking photos at will and eating ice cream we had bought in the gift shops. Skyscrapers poised dominantly overlooking the Falls. There was also a revolving restaurant that offered its patrons a bird's eye view while they sampled the very finest of foods Niagara had to offer. After witnessing one of the world's most famous attractions it was off to Burger King for dinner – there was no McDonalds in sight.

After our feed of junk food, we explored this novel and attractive town. Admiring the dazzling sights and sounds, we bumped into a married couple from Cork. They were on a tour which took them to a load of different places. They had decided to take a trip over the Falls in a helicopter, which was claimed to be the most spectacular way of experiencing them. What a small world, and it proved that no matter where you go on the planet, be it Niagara Falls or the South Pole, you will always meet up with an Irish person.

All the rides and 4D cinema shows were queer expensive, and we hadn't enough to pay for them without having to sacrifice valuable drinking money, and we weren't prepared to do that. On the way to the liquor store we came across a haunted house. I had gone into one of these in Blackpool a few years back, and it scared away any childhood innocence I had left. I convinced the lads to part with ten of their precious dollars as it would be worth it. I hoped it was; I didn't fancy being chased by the newly broke angry mob. Jason greeted us at the door, guiltily gripping a blade in his hand. I stood behind Bruce. The thrilling walk through the house of horrors lasted a few minutes and was decent craic. I forced Nevaeh to lead the way, pushing her on encouragingly to face the monsters that lurked in the darkness. It was fun, and provided an adrenaline rush as you scurried from just about every horror character ever made.

We got our drink – not beer but spirits because the massive store didn't sell beer. Some of the shops sell everything except beer for some peculiar reason. We went back to the room to get changed and showered for our night out. Our room overlooked Main Street, securing front row seats to the action. Tonight we were taking a trip to a strip club. Nevaeh declined our invitation to see naked honeys dancing around us in favour of some sleep instead. It took us some time to find the club, having to repeatedly ask for directions.

There was a sign on the door that outlawed the wearing of articles such as jeans and coloured T-shirts. I was wearing jeans and a green T-shirt, while Bruce was sporting his favourite pink shirt that highlighted his muscular form. We got in. Bruce's bulging biceps must have shaken the door staff and prompted them to allow us entry. Pitchers of beer, good music and live nude dancing – life couldn't get much better. The club was tacky, but in a tasteful way that made you feel at home.

After a while a stripper came over and asked if I'd like a private dance. I glanced around to see a sign that said 'Private Dances $20'. I figured I could just about afford that. She took me into a back room and began dancing provocatively. She slowly removed every item of clothing (which wasn't that many to begin with) to reveal every part of her curvy, hourglass-shaped body.

A few minutes passed and I was getting bored. There was only so much to look at, and I was rather thirsty. Not wanting to be rude, I thought I'd wait till she finished before dashing off for my beer that waited temptingly back on the table. So I closed my eyes and imagined pouring the sweet suds down my throat. Eventually she stopped gesticulating over me and asked if I'd like another dance.

'Ah no that was great.' I quickly replied before she started into another bout of explicit self-expression.

I took out my wallet.

'Twenty isn't it,' already knowing the answer but just to be polite.

'No, it's sixty.'

'What do you mean it's sixty? It says twenty on the sign outside.'

I was getting a little anxious at this stage.

'Well that's for one dance, I gave you three.'

'Did I ask you for three dances.' I came back angrily.

'The bouncers won't let you leave if you don't pay,' she kindly informed me.

Tricked by a girl who took her clothes off for a living: I couldn't believe it. I was shocked she could be this sly and devious as to take advantage of a harmless Irish guy. She wasn't even that bloody good, certainly not worth sixty feckin' dollars – the house of horrors had been more exciting. I had to pay, I couldn't think of a way out, and I could see no fire escapes in the vicinity – coincidence? I think not. They made their livelihood not from stripping but from professional con artistry. This was certainly going to leave me in the doghouse concerning my cash situation. I went back and borrowed $35 from the lads to pay my devoid-of-pleasure debts. I literally threw the money at her, the cunning, heartless exhibitionist.

The lads bought me a couple of beers out of sympathy, and reassured me they would help out if I needed it. Ah, back in the safe, trusting abode of my loyal friends. The three of them chipped in for a table dance from a stripper who was from Rochester. We were speechless. To be honest, she was a little weird herself, and appeared to be halfway to the moon on drugs (or maybe traces of the serum were still in her blood). At that point, I didn't want to see a girl, never mind watch one strip. So I gloomily sat there sipping my over-priced glass of beer, lost in my own thoughts.

Loitering outside for a couple of minutes, Nevaeh, looking dozy and tired, finally opened the door to leave us in. That power nap had done her the world of good – though you wouldn't think it by looking at her. We were all ready to hit the town for some fun. Since I had lost most of my money in the strip joint, we first polished off our stash of jar from the boot of the car and then headed out.

Burger King looked cool with a huge figure of Frankenstein on top, and we couldn't help going in again for some late night supper. We met two girls from Buffalo and we all hung out together for the night. Earlier that day, Michael and I had come across a shop that sold Cuban cigars. We had to buy one as we had never tried them before. America didn't sell them on account of the diplomatic row it still had with Cuba – good old Canada. We sparked them up in the restaurant, and were instantly told by a couple of guys we were talking to that we weren't allowed smoke in there. We shrugged our shoulders and placed them into our mouths. Next thing, about seven other people lit up, and we all sat there happily puffing away.

It took the clinically obese woman behind the counter about five minutes to notice what we were doing.

'You can't smoke in here!' she screamed.

All heads turned to face the snarling manager.

'What, is this not Costa Rica?'

Not impressed with my apparent lack of respect for her authority, she threw the lot of us out. But we made damn sure to bring our chips with us. Otherwise the jolly fat bastard, who had started working there that very day, would have devoured them, no doubt (and he probably would have used the cheese sauce that had been on his face for his newly incarcerated grub).

The clubs were virtually empty as it was a Thursday night. So the two girls brought us to an intimate little bar that resembled an Irish pub. It wasn't strict and, in fact, didn't even bother asking for IDs (maybe it was an Irish bar). It was a relaxing evening as we drained our Canadian beers chatting away among ourselves and to the barmaid. Bruce came down with a severe complaint that night, he broke out in a fit of farts. He couldn't stop. They just kept shootin out his backside and the smell tied in with them was surely dangerous to the health of everyone in the pub. He told us that he wasn't too bothered with holding them in, as the girls weren't exactly what you'd call, his type. We were half cut going to bed, granting a quick and easy lapse into unconsciousness.

Rolling Rock had become our official road trip drink, and 30-packs occupied any free space we had in the wagon. The click of newly opened cans and the hiss that came immediately afterwards gave Stacy that pub feeling as we drove along. This particular drink was probably the gassiest beverage on the planet, even more so than your Fantas and Diet Cokes. One mouthful, and it was a cast-iron certainty to hear an array of different sounds that came from two places of your body.

Nevaeh became the official judge and would rate the noises out of ten. John, who was normally very polite and respectful, won hands down when it came to burping, and often scored full marks for his efforts. With the amount of junk food we were eating, I took the coveted 'skunk' award for the smelliest rudies, with Michael stealing my glory when I wasn't on form (which resulted from eating one burger instead of two). By day five the car reeked of toxic odours and smelled similar to a dump, or knacker camp.

It was fortunate that Nevaeh was the only girl in the car as she was very open-minded and had no qualms about enjoying life. She was more like a ladette who didn't give a fuck what us boys got up to. Any other girl would have been shocked at some of our behaviour (and noises), apart from Emma, who I reckon would have joined in with some rude gestures of her own, and might have even given us a run for our money.

As we drove through the countryside, Michael, for some reason, had looked on the bottle to see where Rolling Rock was made, and then tried to find it on the map. 'Astonishing' was the only word that came to mind as Michael yelped excitedly that the brewery was more or less on our route to Pittsburgh. In such a vast area of land we were no more than an hour away from the home of our beloved drink. It was voted unanimously that Latrobe would be next in line to be graced with our smell – I mean, presence.

Latrobe was a quiet, backward place, and it took numerous attempts to find the brewery when we got there. We pulled into the considerably sized car park but there was no sign of anyone else around. Obviously we were the only ones able to locate it on the map. The factory itself had closed for the day, but we went into the gift shop.

John, who was a Rolling Rock fanatic, had been searching for a T-shirt that bore the name of his favourite tipple for practically the whole summer. He finally found one and bought it the second he laid eyes on it. Compelled to buy something with the logo on it, I purchased a key ring for the car keys back home, while Michael bought a bottle opener – what did you expect, a cross? We explained to the woman working in the gift shop how her drink had become a permanent feature of our seven-day road trip adventure. Out of sheer generosity, she gave Michael a discount on his gift, and threw in a $15 flag that you clipped onto your car window, for free. It was either that or she fancied him, probably the latter I suspected.

Michael had warned us to be careful pulling down the window for fear of losing the flag. He didn't take heed of his own words of wisdom and within an hour of receiving our car mascot, it flew away. To celebrate the death of our beloved flapper, we treated ourselves to a McDonalds. It was just after half ten in the morning and they were still serving breakfast, much to our dismay. Once Michael had left the counter, they began serving lunch. On top of that, they had given Michael the wrong order, and he hated their breakfasts to begin with. He considered going back to express his anger, but the ninety-year old woman working there, who apparently had an Irish temper, deterred him taking such an action.

Pittsburgh was a formidable city with tall skyscrapers and narrow one-way streets. It was attractive and lively, and we were looking forward to sampling the nightlife. Our aim was to find the university, which we eventually did after an hour of trudging the city streets, going around in circles most of the time. The universities in America are akin to little cities. They normally possess everything you could ever want, and this one was no different.

We parked Stacy on the side of the road and went exploring our new surroundings. There was a forty four-storey cathedral on campus, standing proud above the entire city. We climbed the building and the views were powerful. You could see the whole of Pittsburgh going about its business. Albeit they were a lot smaller looking, and you couldn't see precisely what they were doing, but you get the idea.

Outside on the fields, on the grounds belonging to the cathedral, there were people playing frisbie and soccer, and, believe it or not, fellas in their twenties engrossed in a game of hide-and-go-chase. The five of us watched them. It was coming up to eight on a Friday evening, and instead of changing to go out for the night, they were chasing each other around the place like you'd do when you were a kid. Perhaps not every culture has the same obsession with personality-altering liquids as we do. We went back to the car and shoved on our, by now, fairly worn and wrinkled going-out clothes.

Figuring there would be a good choice of bars and restaurants in this youth-orientated area, a pack of girls recommended a pub and invited us to join them for a drink. A good size glass of beer cost just $1. This could be a long night, we agreed. The mood was vivacious, as the bar quickly filled with Friday night revellers (the 'I caught you' kids were nowhere to be seen) looking to have a good time. Michael, while in the toilet, made an acquaintance with some guy who was attending the university. He invited the five of us to a house party taking place later that evening.

Following his scribbled directions, we eventually passed by a mass of houses that were busy hosting parties. You could tell who the popular people were by the amount of students in every house. The whole area, which took the form of a big cul-de-sac, was home to hundreds of students and made for some serious sessions on the weekends. When we got there, the place was chock-a-block with people. We had obviously been invited to the right party. The guy who had invited us welcomed us with open arms, and instructed us to make ourselves at home.

Students crammed into every available space. A band in the corner was keeping the tempo upbeat with live music. Nevaeh later joined them as they were short an unwanted spoons player. We headed out to the back garden. There were four party animals playing a game that involved throwing a ping-pong ball the length of a table trying to get it into a bunch of cups that were laid out in the form of bowling pins. The person who succeeded in guiding the small ball into every cup was declared the winner, and he would then face a different opponent. The thing was, it was meant to be a drinking game, but the guys playing it were so caught up in trying to show off winning, they forgot to drink.

They reluctantly gave me a go after Nevaeh had forced her way in and attempted a few shots, which the nerds didn't appreciate one bit. Bored after a few seconds, we left them play on and went back to our beer – the very essence of being Irish.

Standing outside, quietly sipping our cans, we were approached by a red headed girl. We had put our cases of beer in a heap on the ground and made a circle ensuring their protection. The girl asked Michael for a can and he said no. Word had spread that there were Irish people at the party, and the girl tried to exploit this by literally promoting her roots.

'Look, I'm Irish, too, look at my hair.'

Michael and the rest of us were pissed off by people's continuous claims of being Irish. We had come across so many people all summer who insisted that they were really from Ireland and it was getting very old. Michael snapped and told her she wasn't Irish and to fuck off. He had said what we were all thinking. She got the message and stormed off in a huff – good riddance.

There was one guy who will forever stand out in our minds from that night. He wore a McDonalds T-shirt (which should have been ours) and shorts, was about as fat as a twig, and sported the most horrendous specs since Deirdre from *Coronation Street*. The poor fella didn't know what to do or say. He just walked around the place pretending to fit in, even though he was as out of place as Bill Clinton in a cigarette shop. He was the ultimate nerd, beating the cup boys hands down.

I'm not sure if having the party was illegal, but every now and then, someone would roar 'Cops!' Half the place would leg it out to the back garden and away down the alleyways, while we five watched in amusement and enjoyed our drinks. Strangely enough, the ping-pong boys invited us back to theirs to stay the night. Nevaeh may well have used the implement she nicked from the top of one of the kegs, which apparently was quite expensive, as a bed bargaining chip. Before we left, Michael's worst fear was realised. Distracted by conversation, someone had robbed his drink. In Michael's philosophy this warranted death. He picked up a weapon from the garden, which I think was some sort of huge leaf, and went hunting for his abducted drink. He searched high and low, even the basement, but never found the cans.

On the way back, Bruce, who was langered, called into a pizza restaurant. Five minutes passed and we noticed that Bruce had disappeared. I ran back to find him leaning on the counter waiting for food. He said he had already ordered, but there was no sign of anything cooking. Then the staff said they were closed and Bruce's face crumbled. His expression was priceless as he realised there was no pizza coming. He got angry, insisting he had ordered a few minutes back. Not looking as if they were going to rustle up anything, I assured him that there would be other places to eat, and he decided to leave without a fight.

The house looked like your typical student residence, and the guys put on a bit of music. There was an American football in the room and we started passing it to each other. The lads gave us a telling off, bringing our game to a sudden end (Mr Miagi's influence had been felt far and wide). They were damn annoying and I was quickly starting to lose my mind listening to them. I went upstairs to fetch Nevaeh, who was currently robbing one of the guy's T-shirts. She had tried on a Superman shirt, which happened to be a treasured possession, and ripped it as she pulled it over her head. Mr Ping-pong didn't notice the indiscretion. She handed it back to him, and announced innocently, that there was a tear in it, and wanted a different one. She mooched out of the house sporting another one of his T-shirts, this time a perfectly intact model. It was a job trying to wake Bruce who had conked out on the chair. But I couldn't have stayed there much longer – being squashed in a reeking car had infinitely more appeal.

Stacy finally got the better of us – you could nearly see the grill and headlights form into a smirk. Bruce fell asleep the second he got into the car. The rest of us were eying the forty four-storey cathedral, which we knew stayed open all night (a Friday night bookworm told us as he sat on the third floor studying). We first had to escape the attentions of the security guards, who were on duty making sure no tramps slept there. Michael and John went first, and Nevaeh and myself said we'd meet them on the thirty-third floor.

It felt like *Mission Impossible* as we snuck quietly into the gigantic cathedral that would act as our hotel for the night. We never found the guys, and somehow wound up sleeping in a classroom on the second floor, where the lights turned on automatically when someone entered the room. We lay our sleeping bags on the ground and pulled the cover over us at the top of the class – it was the only time either of us was ever at the top of the class. The lights failed to turn off, but it wasn't too unsettling, that sleeping drug alcohol soon kicked in.

Four hours later, I opened my eyes just a couple of seconds when the door opened, and in walked a student with a bag on her back. Remember, this was a Saturday at eight in the morning. Shock and horror descended on her face as she saw the pair of us lying in bed together. Like a cartoon character leaving a trail of smoke behind, she shot back out and ran down the corridor. I'd say it took no longer than three seconds for us to scoop up our things, belt down the hallway, and fall down the stairs through fits of ludicrous laughter. Michael and John had gone back to the car when there was no sign of us, and kept Bruce company. After finally managing to wake them, by thudding on the window, we were gone with the wind and on our way to the city of Philadelphia.

We pulled up to McDonalds for lunch at one of the service stations off the motorway. When we ate in Burger King the day before, we had all grabbed those plastic hats bearing the Burger King logo, with the intention of going up to the counter in McDonalds and ordering our lunch while wearing these hats. John and I went up and the manager stared disgustingly at us. Another one of the employees looked on with a smile. It was gas, but we were thankful we didn't get snot balls on our cheeseburgers.

We ate on average two meals a day and eleven of those occasions were in a well-known fast food chain. The last time we ate in McDonalds, we all ordered our food. The checkout guy asked Nevaeh what she wanted.

'Cock.' She replied.

The dude behind the counter stood there awkwardly, with an embarrassed look on his face, while we had to block our mouths to disguise our glee. Soon enough word would get round of our unacceptable social behaviour, and we would inevitably be barred from the four billion (or whatever stupid amount) Ronald McDonald chains in the US. But until then keep your eyes open for a blue station wagon pulling into your car park!

The traffic approaching Philly was a nightmare. The colossal roads were littered with thousands of cars each jostling for an advantageous position in the middle of what had turned into the world's biggest car park. To make things worse I was in urgent need of a piss and it was getting worse and worse as time dragged by. The cars were stopped, nothing was moving, and the signposts were still declaring the city to be a few miles away. My bladder was beginning to ache, and my legs were starting to dance to try and relieve some of the pain. I was swerving from lane to lane trying to skip ahead but it didn't seem to be doing much good. I couldn't even get out – there wasn't any hard shoulder to pull in to. The torture was becoming unbearable.

When the chaos began to move, I made every effort to drive as fast as I could to reach the city before I would have to be hospitalised. A speeding ticket no longer held any threat to me. When I did find a spot to park, I leaped out of the car and ran as fast as I could to the nearest building that had a door. Every step I took hurt immensely, and tears streamed down my cheeks as I came to the security guard on the door. I didn't have a clue what the place was but it looked important – possibly a government building. I told him if he didn't let me in to use the toilet, I was going to die. He pulled the door open. I don't think he wanted my death on his conscience. I never ran so fast in my life, and think I left sizzling rubber marks on the gleaming tiled floor. The relief was immeasurable, but at the same time pained like someone had gone to work with a knife on my baby-making parts. Now I knew how Nevaeh felt when it happened to her a few days back. I apologised that I hadn't been more sympathetic towards her in her hour of distress.

Philly was an awesome looking city, full of high-rise buildings and colour. Don't let this apparent splendour throw you because it's a bitch to drive in. We spent a few revolutions of a clock face looking for the city centre. Then, when we eventually found it, it took another age to get to Erin's as we somehow kept going around the same cumbersome roundabout. It was the evening time and we were hungry. As we drove out towards the university where they were living, we spotted a McDonalds. I think we boosted the company's net profit margin a good few percent that week.

We sat down with our couple of dollar burgers, and it dawned on us as we browsed the restaurant that we were the only white people in the whole place. We had stumbled into the ghetto and there wasn't a whitey in sight. Ah well, it was like water off a duck's back. At that point we were used to ending up in just about every hood there was. And anyway, there were burgers to be eaten.

We arranged to meet Erin and her friend (who loved Michael) beside a phone box on campus. I was still suffering from the earlier attack on my organs, and every six or seven seconds I got a shooting, sharp pain through my testicles. The agony didn't relinquish until I had a few jars later that night. Ah, you can always trust the good stuff to sooth whatever is troubling you.

The girls lived a short car journey away in a massive apartment complex in a rundown, dangerous area. A few other girls lived in the flat, which was oddly styled. It was mostly open plan so if there was a fire it would be safer, but it didn't exactly give much privacy if you wanted to get jiggy with someone.

They organised a wee do for our arrival. We had to go to the nearest liquor store as all the Rolling Rock in the car had been consumed along the way. Erin brought us to the dodgiest drink shop in all of Philly. The alcohol was kept behind the counter, guarded by about sixteen layers of bulletproof plastic. You had to ask the shopkeeper to get what you wanted, and then slip the money through a small hole. Again there were no white people around. It was a little intimidating, but all for a good cause. Nevaeh and I went back to the car, which was parked right outside the store. A black lad approached us, and came to the window with a big smile on his face. He asked if Nevaeh was my bitch. Thinking it best to play along I said,

'Ye, she's my bitch, dog,' while trying to conceal the grin that was beginning to break out.

He said you had to have bitches and that I should take care of her, and walked on down the street – what a nice guy.

We made it back without any bullet holes and we were ready to get the party started. Little by little guests began to arrive and the atmosphere sprang to its feet. I got talking to one of the girls who lived there. She asked me where I was from, as she had just come home. I said 'Ireland', and she asked where that was. Okay, it's a small place, not everybody knows where it is. I told her it was in Europe beside England. She then asked what part I was from and I said 'Dublin'.

'Oh Dooblin, I've heard of that place!' she exclaimed fervently.

She was an attractive girl, but after that conversation I lost all interest and went over to Nevaeh instead. Some guys had come in, and one of them was an ugly, hairy son of Vermont. He was wearing an explicit T-shirt that encouraged girls to give him a blowjob and a beer. He wasn't going to get either as it made him out to be a complete weasel. He took it upon himself to rob my coke to mix with his vodka. I let it go the first time but when he repeated the act I became grouchy. His friends also helped themselves to a couple of Michael and Bruce's beers. I went over and told him that it was my bottle of coke, which I had bought for my vodka, and if he continued to rob it, it would be inserted up his backside without the aid of Vaseline.

Not only did he stop drinking it, he went out to the shop and bought me another bottle to show there were no hard feelings. I would have preferred vodka but it was a nice gesture and I let bygones by bygones. That T-shirt he was wearing, by the way, he wasn't wearing it at the end of the night. As, guess who, Nevaeh had somehow managed to convince him to strip off and give it to her (she had started her own exclusive collection of pilfered clothes – none of us would ever be cold again).

Towards the end of the night, John was twisted and had fallen asleep on the couch. Bruce was getting places however, as he disappeared into one of the girl's rooms. He had taken his shirt off, hypnotising her with his lean, muscular body. Michael finally got through to Erin's friend that he was happy with Emma, and wasn't going to cheat on her no matter what state he happened to be in. Though heartbroken, she gave up the ghost. It had been an eventful night overall: Nevaeh had another article of clothing to add to her growing collection; Bruce got lucky with a cute American; John got a good sleep; Michael got rid of his stalker; I got a free bottle of coke;

And the dim girl learned where Ireland was.

The *Rocky* series of films were shot in Philadelphia. We all wanted to visit the stone steps he ran up when training to fight the world champion, Apollo Creed, in the first film. The girls gave us directions, we thanked them for their kind hospitality, and off we ventured. We parked in an abandoned car park a few seconds' walk from the famous steps, right in the middle of a huge roundabout. Since we all had hoodies, we decided to imitate Stallone when he jumped the steps two by two.

Standing at the bottom, we looked up at our challenge. Looking at each other, like racehorses (albeit hung over horses) we started to gallop up the steps taking them two at a time, praying we wouldn't snot ourselves. This was surely harder than it looked when Rocky had completed the task in just one breath. We were exhausted when we reached the summit. Feeling compelled to finish the job we danced around with our arms in the air celebrating our accomplishment. On the grounds of the Philly Art Museum we felt fit and able to take on the Russian tank, Hulk Hogan, or any other adversary who crossed our paths (just need to make sure we were ossified first so we wouldn't feel the pain).

As the sun made everywhere look bright and happy, we took time to admire the tall skyscrapers that conquered the horizon. The park in the foreground was filled with green trees, beautiful fountains, and the magnificent statue that lived in the centre of all the greenery.

A few tourists, mostly American, expressed their admiration for the training exercise we had just endured. They said we looked great as we overcame the illustrious stone steps that Rocky once triumphed. Feeling hot and sweaty, we slipped our shoes and socks off and put our weary legs into the fountain. This didn't quite do the trick, so the five of us embarked on a sort of royal rumble plunging each other into the cool waters, watched by confused passers-by. That was the best wash we had all week, and was about as fresh as we were going to feel. After a bit of football and some rest and relaxation on the grass, we were ready for the long journey back to Boston.

The drive was an arduous affair. We were all tired from the night before, and I was finding it hard to keep my eyes open. We stopped in a garage to ask the mechanic how far it was to Boston, and also to grab a few packets of Doritos. He said it was about four hundred miles. The man was living on a different planet. We had figured it was about three or four hours away, which definitely didn't equate to four hundred miles, probably half that. He must have been from a hillybilly land far away.

There was no point in driving as none of us could concentrate properly. So we parked across the road, took out a few blankets, and went to sleep on a little island of grass. This actually did wonders for us. When we eventually woke up to the annoying bites from vicious ants we had unwittingly sat on, we were energised and ready for the remainder of the trip.

John's relations were putting us up for the night. When we found it (finding specific places in America was bloody hard, damn country was so big), it was pitch dark. They were a lovely family and the youngest daughters were the cutest you were ever likely to meet. We were shown down to the basement, but it was no ordinary basement. It acted as John's uncle's hideaway. It housed a swish leather couch that leaned back if you wanted to peacefully fall asleep, a bar with trinkets of Irish memorabilia, and a barbaric widescreen TV. What a way to finish our road trip – a few beers while watching *XXX*. The film was completely over the top (I just couldn't understand how he made the motorbike fly over the houses with no ramp), but I didn't mind as I fell into a deep sleep halfway through.

From there it was a short hop back to Hyannis. The car had to be returned to its rightful place no later than 2pm that Monday. Stacy had guided us safely around the northeast of America, and had given us probably the best week any of us had ever experienced. Meanwhile, Mumbles was overjoyed when he read the mileage counter on the dashboard, and took great satisfaction in charging us extra, as we had gone over the allotted distance permitted by the firm. There was a glint in his beady eyes as he asked for the additional $275 to cover the twelve hundred and fifty miles. It ached having to pay him, for in our opinion we had paid for the services of the car (he also said that he had to wear a jacket for the first time – shocking).

Hyannis now seemed like a different place. There were still a few Irish people floating about but apart from that it was quiet. You could start to feel the chill in the air. Autumn was coming; Hyannis was beginning to die.

Back in the house there were four survivors: Emma, who was elated at the return of her boyfriend; Shauna; Sheila; and one of Emma's friends from home we met that day. Strange to think that a day separated us from what remained of the summer and having to go home to the life you left behind many moons ago.

Nevaeh and I took the opportunity to take one last tour of the area, to take pictures of everything we hadn't already snapped, which turned out to be most things. We decided to capture our favourite haunt – Christy's twenty-four hour shop with Dunkin Donuts. Outside, Nevaeh went up to a biker and asked if she could sit on his immaculately pristine Harley Davidson while I took a photo, and he agreed to it. As she was getting her leg over, she accidentally karate kicked his helmet from the bike, sending it tumbling down the hill. He suddenly didn't seem so keen on the idea, so we apologised and cycled on before he sued us for damages. That evening we unwound with a few jars, and savoured the last night we'd spend in our treasured home.

Michael and Emma were staying there for another day before their escape to 'the city that never sleeps'. Nevaeh was scheduled to fly home about two hours after me. She was flying to Heathrow and then on to Shannon, while I was going direct to Dublin.

We celebrated the exodus with a few afternoon glasses of whisky and coke, and listened to the songs that had become classics in their own right. Mocha came over to bid us a last farewell, or me anyway, for Michael and Emma would stay with him for a couple of nights after their city break. They would be the last to leave and didn't return to Ireland until the twentieth. Seeing the site where the Twin Towers once stood, two years on to the very minute, would be eerie. They would find themselves reliving that seminal morning – trying to understand why, changes that came about, etching a new philosophy.

There was a sense of loss as Nevaeh and I pulled up to the transportation centre to catch the bus that would take us to our last destination in America – Logan Airport. Hugs and sombre 'see ya laters' were exchanged with Michael and Emma. It was time to board the bus and leave Hyannis for good.

We met Jeanie and Matilda in the airport, in McDonalds (where else?). They were on the flight preceding Nevaeh's, so we joined them for the last supper. Their gate was called almost as soon as we had sat down. It worked out well, though, as they didn't have time to finish their food, so it was rightfully passed on to us. We inherited two big drinks that were mostly full, a fistful of chips, and a few sachets of sweet and sour sauce. Matilda was also forced to leave her Sushi behind (she was always a good eater). I went with the old motto 'waste not want not', and devoured the defenceless raw fish. We hung around for a while talking of the good times we'd had, and what we were going to do when we got home; which, at that moment, didn't seem important.

The PA system sprang to life once more and announced that boarding for my flight was commencing. The moment had come. It was time to go home. An air of finality, sorrow now lingered. We hugged each other tight, wishing we could turn back the clock. But we couldn't. Melancholy, lip-twitching smiles were all that were left. Nevaeh turned and walked away, looking back once for a last wave of goodbye. Handing my ticket to the hostess, I began my lonely walk down the tunnel to the plane that would land in reality. I knew, there and then, that a truly magical and special era had come to an end.

Some bits of Wisdom I've acquired that I'd like to pass on.

1. Bring Barry's Tea, as coffee is the preferred drink in America.

2. Bring plenty of deodorant. Come July, the humidity is severe and sweating begins as soon as you step out of the shower.

3. Never use bleach on CLOTHES.

4. Accept that hunger is a good and natural feeling.

5. Bring some knee and elbow pads, and any other part of your body you cherish, as chances are, either drunk or sober, you will at some stage fall off your bike.

6. Learn to love McDonalds.

7. Make an appointment to have your liver checked when you get home.

8. Make sure you have someone (or befriend someone) who is twenty-one so they can buy you drink from the liquor store.

9. Terrorise Mr Miagi.

10. Let down the air in some of the cars in the rent-a-car company. Then go in and talk to Mumbles about the weather.

11. NEVER, EVER, TRUST STRIPPERS.

12. Steal drinks from fast food places. It's just a waste of money paying for them.

13. If you manage to rent our house take good care of her, and she will show you great times in return.

14. If you happen to spot Nevaeh, run. She will have no problem convincing you to buy her a bagel, and if you refuse, she will rob you.

15. Hide drink outside clubs for afterwards, dancing builds quite a thirst.

16. If you caddy at the course ask for Mocha's putter. I lost it one evening and forgot to get it back. Also, stay away from the girl at the halfway house – she's mine.

17. If a farting competition commences, make sure to drink Rolling Rock. You will win.

18. If you're a guy, watch your back – lots of gays around.

19. Have two scorpion bowls – if you're brave enough.

20. If you happen to rent Stacy, treat her with the smells of alcohol mixed with the gases from your body she deserves.

21. Go and have the summer of your lives, and I'll see you all in Pufferbellies!